CULTURE SHOCK

RESPONDING TO TODAY'S MOST CONTROVERSIAL ISSUES

CULTURE SHOCK

TABLE OF CONTENTS

HOW TO START YOUR OWN SMALL GROUP

The fact that you are even reading this page says a lot about you. It says that you are either one of those people who has to read everything, or it says you are open to God using you to lead a group.

Leading a small group can sound intimidating, but it really doesn't have to be. Think of it more as gathering a few friends to get to know each other better and to have some discussion around spiritual matters.

Here are a few practical tips to help you get started:

1. **Pray** — One of the most important principles of spiritual leadership is to realize you can't do this on your own. No matter how long you've been a Christian or been involved in ministry, you need the power of the Holy Spirit. Lean on Him...He will help you.

2. **Invite some friends** — Don't be afraid to ask people to come to your group. You will be surprised how many people are open to a study like this. Whether you have 4 or 14 in your group, it can be a powerful experience. You should probably plan on at least an hour and a half for your group meeting.

3. **Get your materials** — You will need to get a DVD of the video teaching done by Chip Ingram. You can get the DVD from www.livingontheedge.org. Also, it will be helpful for each person to have their own study guide. You can also purchase those through the website.

4. **Watch the Coaching Videos** — We have put together a brief video for each session that will give you a couple of tips about facilitating that week's study. Log onto www.LivingOnTheEdge.org/CultureShockCoaching.

5. **Be prepared to facilitate** — Just a few minutes a week in preparation can make a huge difference in the group experience. Each week, preview the video teaching and review the discussion questions. If you don't think your group can get through all the questions, select the ones that are most relevant to your group.

6. **Learn to say "I don't know"** — This series takes on some of the most difficult questions that Christians and non-Christians struggle with. These sessions will spark some lively and spirited discussions. When tough questions come up, it's ok for you to say "I don't know." Take the pressure off. No one expects you to have all the answers.

7. **Love your group** — Maybe the most important thing you bring to the group is your personal care for them. If you will pray for them, encourage them, call them, e-mail them, involve them, and love them, God will be pleased and you will have a very meaningful experience.

Thank you for your availability. May God bless you as you serve Him by serving others.

HOW TO GET THE MOST OUT OF THIS EXPERIENCE

You are about to begin a powerful journey exploring some of the most controversial issues of our generation. This powerful series taught by Chip Ingram provides in-depth teaching as well as challenging, practical application.

Below, you will find a list of each week's segments as well as some hints for getting the most out of this experience. If you are leading the group, you will find some additional help and coaching on page 115.

1. TAKE IT IN

It is important for us to get "before God" and submit ourselves to his truth. During this section you will watch the video teaching by Chip. He will introduce each session with a personal word to the group followed by the teaching portion of the video. At the end of the teaching segment, Chip will wrap up the session and help the group dive into discussion.

A teaching outline with fill-ins is provided for each session. As you follow along, write down questions or insights that you can share during the discussion time.

Even though most of the verses will appear on the screen and in your notes, it is a great idea to bring your own Bible each week. It will allow you to make notes in your own Bible and find other passages that might be relevant to that week's study.

2. TALK IT OVER

We not only grow by listening to God's word, but we grow "in community." The friendship and insights of those in the group will enrich your small group experience. Several discussion questions are provided for your group to further engage the teaching content. Keep the following guidelines in mind for having a healthy group discussion.

- **Be involved.** Jump in and share your thoughts. Your ideas are important and you have a perspective that is unique and can benefit the other group members.
- **Be a good listener.** Value what others are sharing. Seek to really understand the perspective of others in your group and don't be afraid to ask follow up questions.
- **Be courteous.** People hold strong opinions about the topics in this study. Spirited discussion is great. Disrespect and attack is not. When there is disagreement, focus on the issue and never turn the discussion into a personal attack.
- **Be focused.** Stay on topic. Help the group explore the subject at hand and try to save unrelated questions or stories for afterwards.

- **Be careful not to dominate.** Be aware of the amount of talking you are doing in proportion to the rest of the group and make space for others to speak.
- **Be a learner.** Stay sensitive to what God might be wanting to teach you through the lesson, as well as through what others have to say. Focus more on your own growth rather than making a point or winning an argument.

3. LIVE IT OUT

BIO is a word that is synonymous with "life". The key to helping you become the person God wants you to be is found in these three simple letters: B.I.O.

B = COME "**BEFORE GOD**" DAILY

Meet with Him personally through His word and prayer to enjoy His presence, receive His direction, and follow His will.

I = DO LIFE "**IN COMMUNITY**" WEEKLY

Structure your week to personally connect in safe relationships that provide love, support, transparency, challenge, and accountability.

O = BE "**ON MISSION**" 24/7

Cultivate a mindset to "live out" Jesus' love for others through acts of sacrifice and service at home, work, play, and church.

4. ACCELERATE *(20 minutes that turn concepts into convictions)*

Inspiration comes from hearing God's Word; **motivation** grows by discussing God's Word; **transformation** occurs when you study it for yourself.

If you want to "accelerate" your growth, here is an assignment you can do at home each week. Our convictions become even stronger when we dig into Scripture and discover truth for ourselves. To help you get the most out of this exercise, consider partnering up with somebody in your group who will also commit to do the assignment this week. Then, after you have each done the assignment, agree to spend 10 minutes by phone to share what you learned and what you are applying.

SESSION ONE

WHATEVER HAPPENED TO RIGHT & WRONG?
PART 1

TAKE IT IN

We've Got A Problem!

- The Symptom = Our Moral ______________________________.
- The Issue = Ethics and ______________________________.
- The Dilemma = Who's to say what's ______________________ and wrong?
- The Question = What is ______________________________?

UNDERSTANDING THE REAL PROBLEM:

Diagnosis – Our view of truth has dramatically shifted in the last 50-60 years.

- Among Intellectuals:
  Mere Christianity by C. S. Lewis
- In Education:
  The Closing of the American Mind by Allan Bloom
- In Law & Science:
  Reason in the Balance: The Case Against Naturalism in Science, Law, and Education by Phillip E. Johnson
- In Culture:
  Escape from Reason and The God Who Is There by Francis A. Schaeffer

SUMMARIZING THE TWO MODELS OF TRUTH:

"Truth is Relative"
Existential Concept of Truth

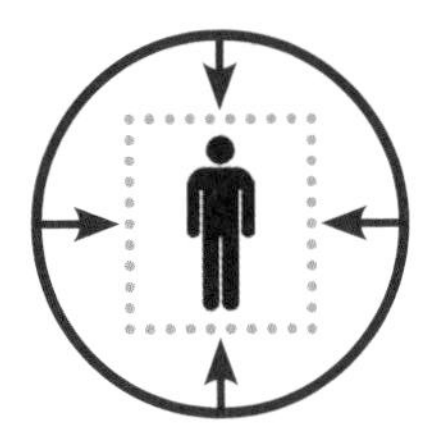

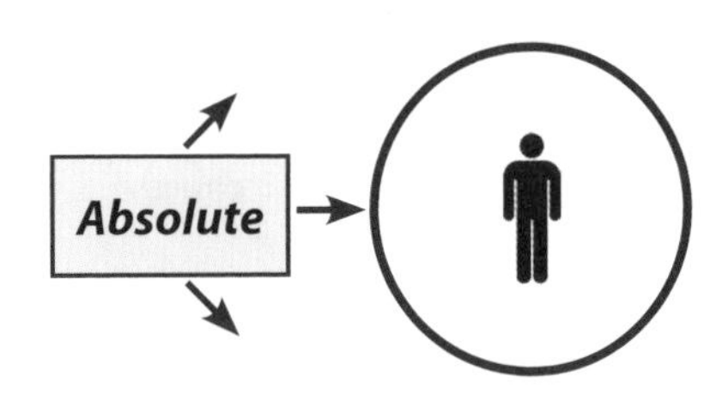

This circle represents our experience. The dotted square is truth as the individual perceives it to be for himself through his experience.

This circle represents our experience. The rectangle represents unchanging truth that is absolute. It affects the realm of our experience, but is just as true in its effect on all of life, whether experienced or not.

Pluralism = all opinions have equal value.

The #1 virtue of relative truth is ______________________________.

TALK IT OVER

1. What is the biggest moral shift you've seen in your lifetime?

2. Share some examples of things that used to be considered absolute truth, but now they are relative.

3. How do you respond to Chip's statement that we have a problem in the church? Why do you think the church hasn't been effective in stemming the tide of relativism?

4. How do you think this drift toward relativism has impacted you personally? Your kids? Your grandchildren? Your church?

LIVE IT OUT – B.I.O.

BIO is a word that is synonymous with "life". The key to helping you become the person God wants you to be is found in these three simple letters: B.I.O.

B = COME "**BEFORE GOD**" DAILY

Meet with Him personally through His word and prayer to enjoy His presence, receive His direction, and follow His will.

I = DO LIFE "IN COMMUNITY" WEEKLY

Structure your week to personally connect in safe relationships that provide love, support, transparency, challenge, and accountability.

O = BE "ON MISSION" 24/7

Cultivate a mindset to "live out" Jesus' love for others through acts of sacrifice and service at home, work, play, and church.

COME BEFORE GOD

5. Have someone in the group read Psalm 119:89-96. What words in this passage describe God's unchanging truth? What phrase or verse most challenges you personally? Why?

DO LIFE IN COMMUNITY

6. What specific things can your group do to help challenge you to become a better "thinker" when it comes to our faith? Make a list of 2 or 3 ideas.

BE ON MISSION

7. What action step will you take this week in order to get better equipped to know what you believe and why you believe it? (i.e. download a message to listen to, read a chapter of a doctrinal book, or review this message privately)

ACCELERATE *(20 minutes that turn concepts into convictions)*

Inspiration comes from hearing God's Word; motivation grows by discussing God's Word; transformation occurs when you study it for yourself.

If you want to "accelerate" your growth, here is an assignment you can do this week. To help you get the most out of this exercise, consider partnering up with somebody in your group who will also commit to do the assignment this week. Then, after you have each done the assignment, agree to spend 10 minutes by phone to share what you learned and what you are applying.

COME BEFORE GOD

1. Read the following passage carefully and slowly.

[1]My son, if you accept my words and store up my commands within you, [2]turning your ear to wisdom and applying your heart to understanding, [3]and if you call out for insight and cry aloud for understanding, [4]and if you look for it as for silver and search for it as for hidden treasure, [5]then you will understand the

fear of the LORD and find the knowledge of God. [6]For the LORD gives wisdom, and from his mouth come knowledge and understanding.

PROVERBS 2:1-6 (NIV)

2. Go through this passage and circle all of the verbs.

3. Now, go through the passage and underline all the words or phrases that are synonymous with God's truth.

4. How would you describe your appetite for God's truth? What currently is keeping you from searching for it as for hidden treasure? When is the best time of the day for you to read/study God's Word personally?

DO LIFE IN COMMUNITY

5. Get together with a Christian friend this week or plan a 15 minute phone call and have the following conversation. Share one significant truth you are learning from God's Word and one cultural issue that you would like to understand and be able to articulate from a Christian worldview.

BE ON MISSION

6. During this week's session, Chip challenged us to have some conversations around the dinner table about why you believe what you believe. Select one "absolute truth" that you can share with your family or friends around the dinner table this week. Help them not only know what you believe, but also what is the basis for your belief about that truth.

SESSION TWO

WHATEVER HAPPENED TO RIGHT & WRONG?
PART 2

CULTURE SHOCK

TAKE IT IN

WHAT HAPPENED?

- Historical Analysis
- Philosophical Analysis

HOW DID IT HAPPEN?

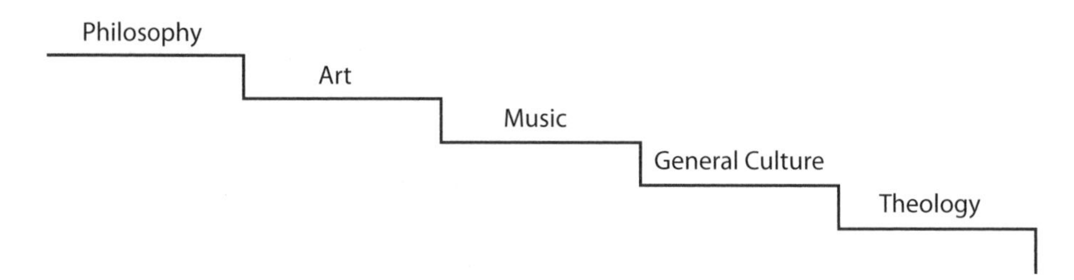

HOW IS THE RELATIVE TRUTH VS ABSOLUTE TRUTH CONFLICT PLAYED OUT DAILY?

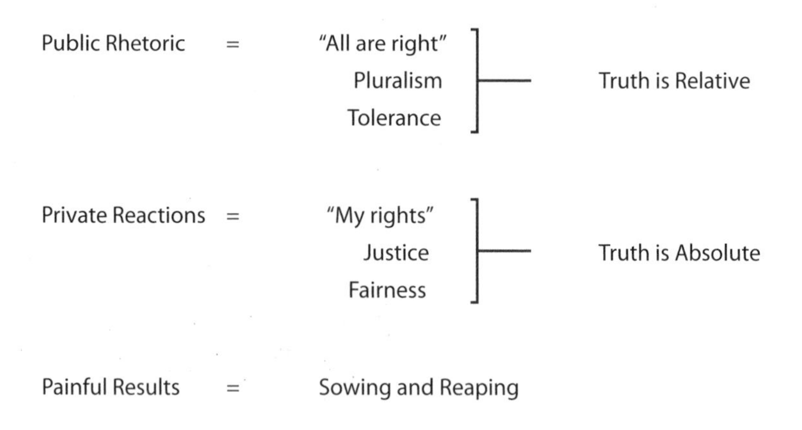

Painful Results = Sowing and Reaping

[7]"Do not be deceived: God cannot be mocked. A man reaps what he sows. [8]The one who sows to please his sinful nature, from that nature will reap destruction; the one who sows to please the Spirit, from the Spirit will reap eternal life."

GALATIANS 6:7-8 (NIV)

What did Jesus Say About Truth?

- Jesus' outrageous ______________________...
    1. About Himself. (John 14:6)
    2. About His Word. (John 17:17)

- Jesus' outrageous ______________________...
    1. About you. (John 4:23)
    2. About your welfare. (John 8:32)

TALK IT OVER

1. What is the difference between absolute truth and relative truth and why does it matter?

2. Chip read a letter from a high school student who said "everyone is entitled to their own subjective reality." If you could sit down with that student, what would you say in response to that statement?

3. Chip said there are painful consequences to relativism. What are some examples where our society is bearing the painful consequences of relativism? How is this impacting the church?

4. Where are you or your children being subtly influenced to embrace "relative truth"?

LIVE IT OUT – B.I.O.

BIO is a word that is synonymous with "life". The key to helping you become the person God wants you to be is found in these three simple letters: B.I.O.

B = COME "BEFORE GOD" DAILY

Meet with Him personally through His word and prayer to enjoy His presence, receive His direction, and follow His will.

I = DO LIFE "IN COMMUNITY" WEEKLY

Structure your week to personally connect in safe relationships that provide love, support, transparency, challenge, and accountability.

O = BE "ON MISSION" 24/7

Cultivate a mindset to "live out" Jesus' love for others through acts of sacrifice and service at home, work, play, and church.

COME BEFORE GOD

5. The high school student's letter that Chip read stated, "All religions are right for particular groups… but there is no one religion that is right for everyone."

   Yet, in John 14:6 Jesus said, *"I am the way and the truth and the life. No one comes to the Father except through me."*

   How would you answer someone who challenges Jesus' claim that only through Him can you get to heaven? What is your conviction on this radical claim?

DO LIFE IN COMMUNITY

6. Chip said the church is full of pragmatists (reducing life to what works vs. what's right). Where has pragmatism and consumerism infiltrated your life? Family? Church? Stop and pray for your pastor, your church leadership and your church as God leads you.

BE ON MISSION

7. Suppose that a conversation comes up this week at the office regarding the subject of homosexuality. Someone turns to you and asks what you personally believe about homosexuality. What would you say and how would you take your stand in a way that modeled both "truth and grace"?

ACCELERATE *(20 minutes that turn concepts into convictions)*

Inspiration comes from hearing God's Word; motivation grows by discussing God's Word; transformation occurs when you study it for yourself.

If you want to "accelerate" your growth, here is an assignment you can do this week. To help you get the most out of this exercise, consider partnering up with somebody in your group who will also commit to do the assignment this week. Then, after you have each done the assignment, agree to spend 10 minutes by phone to share what you learned and what you are applying.

COME BEFORE GOD

1. Read the following passage carefully and slowly.

> *[137]Righteous are you, O LORD, and your laws are right. [138]The statutes you have laid down are righteous; they are fully trustworthy. [139]My zeal wears me out, for my enemies ignore your words. [140]Your promises have been thoroughly tested, and your servant loves them. [141]Though I am lowly*

and despised, I do not forget your precepts. [142]Your righteousness is everlasting and your law is true. [143]Trouble and distress have come upon me, but your commands are my delight. [144]Your statutes are forever right; give me understanding that I may live.

PSALM 119:137-144 (NIV)

2. Circle all the phrases that speak to the credibility of God's truth.

3. From this passage, what are some of the personal benefits of knowing and following God's truth?

4. All your words are true; all your righteous laws are eternal. Psalm 119:160 (NIV) What do you know to be true about God's laws? Take a few moments and write down your thoughts.

    - *For example: God's laws are always intended for my best.*
    -
    -
    -
    -
    -

DO LIFE IN COMMUNITY

5. Knowing God's Word is critical to standing against relativism. Get together with or schedule a call with someone from your small group. Share with them where you need to "shore up" your understanding of the Bible. Share your current game plan and ask for their help in keeping you accountable.

BE ON MISSION

6. Schedule a discussion with your family about relativism. Identify one way that relativism is working against your family. Ask family members or friends where they feel the most pressure to conform to the world's relative standards. Discuss ways to support one another in walking in the truth.

SESSION THREE

THE SEARCH FOR TRUTH ABOUT SEX
PART 1

TAKE IT IN

Never in the history of the world has a culture shifted its values concerning sexuality as rapidly or as drastically as it has in America in the last 50 years.

WHAT HAPPENED?

- The Shift
- The Causes
- The Impact
- The Cost

Myth #1 – God Is anti-sex.

Truth = God is so pro-sex He ________________________ it to provide...

- Physical Pleasure (Genesis 1:26-27)
- Procreation (Genesis 1:27)
- Relational Intimacy (Genesis 2:18-24)
- Spiritual Object Lesson (Ephesians 5:31-32)

Myth #2 – Christians' sex lives and views of sex are dull, boring and "out of touch."

Truth = The Scriptures command God's people to be downright ________________ in their marital love.

> *[18]May your fountain be blessed, and may you rejoice in the wife of your youth. [19]A loving doe, a graceful deer — may her breasts satisfy you always, may you ever be captivated by her love.*
>
> PROVERBS 5:18-19 (NIV)

[2]But since there is so much immorality, each man should have his own wife, and each woman her own husband. [3]The husband should fulfill his marital duty to his wife, and likewise the wife to her husband. [4]The wife's body does not belong to her alone but also to her husband. In the same way, the husband's body does not belong to him alone but also to his wife. [5]Do not deprive each other except by mutual consent and for a time, so that you may devote yourselves to prayer. Then come together again so that Satan will not tempt you because of your lack of self-control.

---

1 CORINTHIANS 7:2-5 (NIV)

Myth #3 – As long as people love each other, sex is okay with God.

Truth = The Bible actually ______________________________ all sexual relationships outside of marriage.

- *"You shall not commit adultery."*
  (Exodus 20:14)
- *"Abstain from ... sexual immorality."*
  (Acts 15:29)
- *"Flee from sexual immorality."*
  (1 Corinthians 6:18)
- *"We should not commit sexual immorality."*
  (1 Corinthians 10:8)
- *"But among you there must not be even a hint of sexual immorality ... "*
  (Ephesians 5:3)
- *"It is God's will that you ... should avoid sexual immorality."*
  (1 Thessalonians 4:3)

TALK IT OVER

(For the discussion time, if you are a mixed gender group, separate into men's and women's groups.)

1. What was your family's mindset or your church's mindset when it came to sex? What lens have you looked at sex through as you've grown up?

2. In your lifetime, what do you believe has been the single biggest shift in people's view of sexuality?

3. In what ways have we as a culture/church become desensitized to distorted views of sex and sexuality?

LIVE IT OUT - B.I.O.

BIO is a word that is synonymous with "life". The key to helping you become the person God wants you to be is found in these three simple letters: B.I.O.

B = COME "**BEFORE GOD**" DAILY

Meet with Him personally through His word and prayer to enjoy His presence, receive His direction, and follow His will.

I = DO LIFE "**IN COMMUNITY**" WEEKLY

Structure your week to personally connect in safe relationships that provide love, support, transparency, challenge, and accountability.

O = BE "**ON MISSION**" 24/7

Cultivate a mindset to "live out" Jesus' love for others through acts of sacrifice and service at home, work, play, and church.

COME BEFORE GOD

> *[13]The body is not meant for sexual immorality, but for the Lord, and the Lord for the body. [14]By his power God raised the Lord from the dead, and he will raise us also. [15]Do you not know that your bodies are members of Christ himself? Shall I then take the members of Christ and unite them with a prostitute? Never! [16]Do you not know that he who unites himself with a prostitute is one with her in body? For it is said, "The two will become one flesh." [17]But he who unites himself with the Lord is one with him in spirit.*
>
> 1 CORINTHIAN 6:13-17 (NIV)

4. Why do you think Paul speaks about the resurrection in the middle of a passage about sexual immorality? What temptations and cultural values were the Corinthian believers facing that required such supernatural power?

5. What does this passage in 1 Corinthians 6:13-17 teach us about the "body" and the implications of physical intimacy?

DO LIFE IN COMMUNITY

6. In Ephesians 5:3, Paul says, *"among you there must not be even a hint of sexual immorality..."* In your life, what bait does Satan use to lure you toward sexual sin?

BE ON MISSION

7. Decide today to become a champion for sexual purity. Sit down with those who look to your for spiritual leadership (your children, a niece, a nephew, a roommate or a person you are discipling) and have an honest conversation about God's standard for sexual purity. What will you say to them? What resources do you need to do this well?

ACCELERATE *(20 minutes that turn concepts into convictions)*

Inspiration comes from hearing God's Word; motivation grows by discussing God's Word; transformation occurs when you study it for yourself.

If you want to "accelerate" your growth, here is an assignment you can do this week. To help you get the most out of this exercise, consider partnering up with somebody in your group who will also commit to do the assignment this week. Then, after you have each done the assignment, agree to spend 10 minutes by phone to share what you learned and what you are applying.

COME BEFORE GOD

1. Read the following passage carefully and slowly.

> *[1]Be imitators of God, therefore, as dearly loved children [2]and live a life of love, just as Christ loved us and gave himself up for us as a fragrant offering and sacrifice to God. [3]But among you there must not be even a hint of sexual immorality, or of any kind of*

impurity, or of greed, because these are improper for God's holy people. [4]Nor should there be obscenity, foolish talk or coarse joking, which are out of place, but rather thanksgiving. [5]For of this you can be sure: No immoral, impure or greedy person—such a man is an idolater —has any inheritance in the kingdom of Christ and of God. [6]Let no one deceive you with empty words, for because of such things God's wrath comes on those who are disobedient. [7]Therefore do not be partners with them. [8]For you were once darkness, but now you are light in the Lord. Live as children of light [9](for the fruit of the light consists in all goodness, righteousness and truth) [10]and find out what pleases the Lord. [11]Have nothing to do with the fruitless deeds of darkness, but rather expose them. [12]For it is shameful even to mention what the disobedient do in secret. [13]But everything exposed by the light becomes visible, [14]for it is light that makes everything visible. This is why it is said: "Wake up, O sleeper, rise from the dead, and Christ will shine on you." [15]Be very careful, then, how you live —not as unwise but as wise, [16]making the most of every opportunity, because the days are evil.

EPHESIANS 5:1-16 (NIV)

2. Why are verses 1 and 2 a great foundation for Paul's challenge about sexual purity? What's the difference between love and lust?

3. In verse 11 Paul says "have nothing to do with the fruitless deeds of darkness, but rather expose them." Why would God want us to "expose" the fruitless deed of darkness? (To help answer this, go back and read verses 8-14.)

DO LIFE IN COMMUNITY

4. Get together with a trusted friend this week and have a discussion around Ephesians 5:1-16. Read the passage with your friend and then talk about what it looks like practically to "live wisely." Share your personal pre-decisions about what you will view and how you will relate to the opposite sex to maintain sexual purity. Confess and ask for help in any areas of your life that fall short of God's standard for sexual purity.

BE ON MISSION

5. Spend some time praying for someone who you know is living contrary to God's view of sex. You may feel powerless to help that person embrace God's view of sexuality, but your prayers can make a difference.

SESSION FOUR

THE SEARCH FOR TRUTH ABOUT SEX
PART 2

CULTURE SHOCK

TAKE IT IN

REVIEW FROM SESSION 3

Myth #1 – God is anti-sex.

Myth #2 – Christians' sex lives and views are dull, boring and "out of touch."

Myth #3 – As long as people love each other, sex is okay with God.

Myth #4 – Only a "cosmic killjoy" totally out of touch with today's culture and people's needs would prohibit all sex outside of marriage.

Truth = God prohibits all immoral behavior outside of marriage because of His desire to...

- ______________________________ you. (Romans 6:23)
- ______________________________ for you. (Jeremiah 29:11)

> *For I know the plans I have for you," declares the LORD, "plans to prosper you and not to harm you, plans to give you hope and a future.*
>
> JEREMIAH 29:11 (NIV)

Myth #5 – Everyone needs to "sow their wild oats" and experiment sexually before they settle down in a long-term relationship.

Truth = Sexual sins have uniquely ______________________________ impact on people's lives because...

- It's a sin against ______________________________. (1 Corinthians 6:16-20)

> *[16]Do you not know that he who unites himself with a prostitute is one with her in body? For it is said, "The two will become one flesh." [17]But he who unites himself with the Lord is one with him in spirit. [18]Flee*

from sexual immorality. All other sins a man commits are outside his body, but he who sins sexually sins against his own body. [19]Do you not know that your body is a temple of the Holy Spirit, who is in you, whom you have received from God? You are not your own; [20]you were bought at a price. Therefore honor God with your body.

1 CORINTHIANS 6:16-20 (NIV)

- It's a sin whose roots are in spiritual rebellion and ______________________. (Ephesians 5:3-7)

[3]But among you there must not be even a hint of sexual immorality, or of any kind of impurity, or of greed, because these are improper for God's holy people. [4]Nor should there be obscenity, foolish talk or coarse joking, which are out of place, but rather the giving of thanks. [5]For of this you can be sure: No immoral, impure or greedy person—such a man is an idolater—has any inheritance in the kingdom of Christ and of God. [6]Let no one deceive you with empty words, for because of such things God's wrath comes on those who are disobedient. [7]Therefore do not be partners with them.

EPHESIANS 5:3-7 (NIV)

- When your sexual practice is opposed to what God says,

  you are worshipping ______________________.

Myth #6 – It's too late for me — sexual sin is so powerful, nothing can loosen its grip on my life.

Truth = Christ died to pay for the ______________________ of your sin and break its ______________________ in your life.

- **Step #1 – Be Honest**

  The LORD is near to all who call on him, to all who call on him in truth.

  PSALM 145:18 (NIV)

- **Step #2 – Repent/Confess**

  If we confess our sins, he is faithful and just and will forgive us our sins and purify us from all unrighteousness.

  I JOHN 1:9 (NIV)

- **Step #3 – Forsake It**

  He who conceals his sins does not prosper, but whoever confesses and renounces them finds mercy.

  PROVERBS 28:13 (NIV)

TALK IT OVER

(For the discussion time, if you are a mixed gender group, separate into men's and women's groups.)

1. What most stood out to you from Chip's teaching? Why?

2. What are some of the residual negative consequences of sexual sin in a person's life?

3. Controlling your thought life is crucial to sexual purity. As a group review the following verse:

> *Finally, brothers, whatever is true, whatever is noble, whatever is right, whatever is pure, whatever is lovely, whatever is admirable — if anything is excellent or praiseworthy — think about such things.*
>
> PHILIPPIANS 4:8 (NIV)

How can each phrase of this passage be an effective weapon in the fight for sexual purity?

4. What kind of guardrails do you need to put into your life so that, as Paul said, there won't be even a "hint" of sexual immorality?

LIVE IT OUT – B.I.O.

BIO is a word that is synonymous with "life". The key to helping you become the person God wants you to be is found in these three simple letters: B.I.O.

B = COME "**BEFORE GOD**" DAILY

Meet with Him personally through His word and prayer to enjoy His presence, receive His direction, and follow His will.

I = DO LIFE "**IN COMMUNITY**" WEEKLY

Structure your week to personally connect in safe relationships that provide love, support, transparency, challenge, and accountability.

O = BE "**ON MISSION**" 24/7

Cultivate a mindset to "live out" Jesus' love for others through acts of sacrifice and service at home, work, play, and church.

COME BEFORE GOD

> *[18]Flee from sexual immorality. All other sins a man commits are outside his body, but he who sins*

sexually sins against his own body. [19]Do you not know that your body is a temple of the Holy Spirit, who is in you, whom you have received from God? You are not your own; [20]you were bought at a price. Therefore honor God with your body.

1 CORINTHIANS 6:18-20 (NIV)

5. Chip said, "If you are a follower of Jesus, his temple is your physical body." How should that truth motivate us to sexual purity? Discuss the close relationship between worship, sexuality, and spirituality?

DO LIFE IN COMMUNITY

6. What accountability do you need from this group to help you stay sexually pure? Or who is it in your life that you will be totally honest with and accountable to regarding your sexual purity?

BE ON MISSION

7. Your sexual purity is a powerful testimony to the world of God's truth and power. Close this session by praying for one another… and pray specifically for struggles and temptations that have been shared by those in your group.

ACCELERATE *(20 minutes that turn concepts into convictions)*

Inspiration comes from hearing God's Word; motivation grows by discussing God's Word; transformation occurs when you study it for yourself.

If you want to "accelerate" your growth, here is an assignment you can do this week. To help you get the most out of this exercise, consider partnering up with somebody in your group who will also commit to do the assignment this week. Then, after you have each done the assignment, agree to spend 10 minutes by phone to share what you learned and what you are applying.

COME BEFORE GOD

1. Read the following passage carefully and slowly.

> *[16]So I say, live by the Spirit, and you will not gratify the desires of the sinful nature. [17]For the sinful nature desires what is contrary to the Spirit, and the Spirit what is contrary to the sinful nature. They are in conflict with each other, so that you do not do what you want.*
>
> GALATIANS 5:16-17 (NIV)

> *Do not conform any longer to the pattern of this world, but be transformed by the renewing of your mind. Then you will be able to test and approve what God's will is — his good, pleasing and perfect will.*
>
> ROMANS 12:2 (NIV)

Run from anything that stimulates youthful lusts. Instead, pursue righteous living, faithfulness, love, and peace. Enjoy the companionship of those who call on the Lord with pure hearts.

2 TIMOTHY 2:22 (NLT)

2. What are some strategies you can deduce from these passages that would be beneficial in the pursuit of sexual purity?

3. In Galatians 5:16-17, Paul says that we are to "live or walk by the Spirit." What does Paul mean by these statements?

4. In Romans 12:2, Paul says "Do not conform any longer to the pattern of this world." According to the second half of that verse, what solution does Paul offer? How does renewing your mind and living by the Spirit work together?

DO LIFE IN COMMUNITY

5. This week sign up for an internet filter for your computer. These filters will flag any inappropriate site you visit and send a report to the person you have asked to help keep you accountable. So, identify and ask the person that will get your report. A couple of good options are www.xxxchurch.com and www.covenanteyes.com.

BE ON MISSION

6. From these passages, what is God directing you to do? What step of faith/ obedience do you need to take to experience His good, acceptable, and perfect will in your life?

SESSION FIVE

WHAT DO YOU SAY TO A GAY FRIEND?
PART 1

TAKE IT IN

Understanding The Issue = 2 Positions

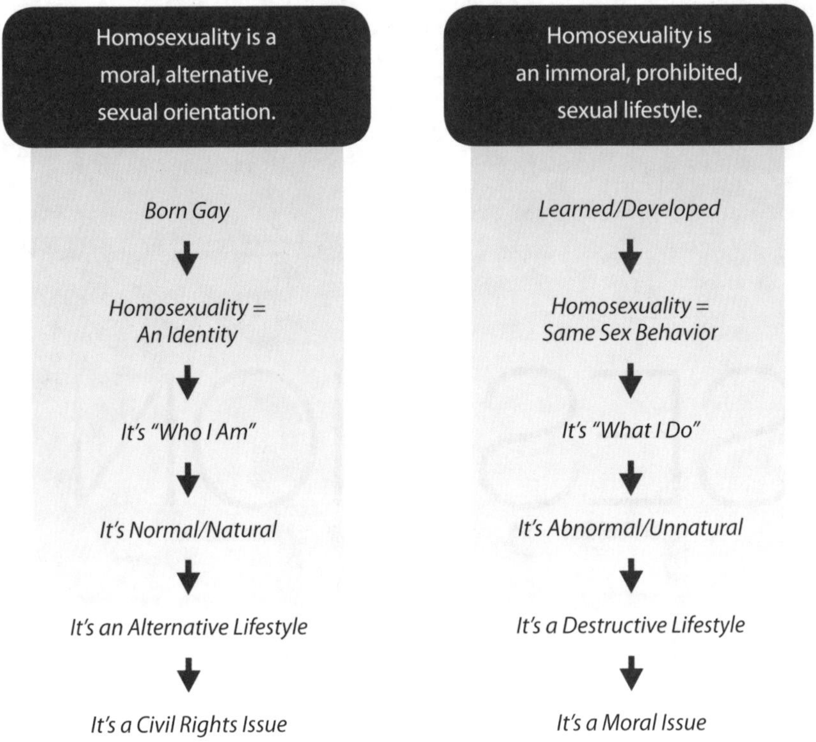

Homosexuality is a moral, alternative, sexual orientation.	Homosexuality is an immoral, prohibited, sexual lifestyle.
Born Gay	*Learned/Developed*
↓	↓
Homosexuality = An Identity	*Homosexuality = Same Sex Behavior*
↓	↓
It's "Who I Am"	*It's "What I Do"*
↓	↓
It's Normal/Natural	*It's Abnormal/Unnatural*
↓	↓
It's an Alternative Lifestyle	*It's a Destructive Lifestyle*
↓	↓
It's a Civil Rights Issue	*It's a Moral Issue*

Premise #1 – I was __________________________________ this way.

- Genetic Factors
- Developmental Factors
- Environmental Factors

Premise #2 – ____________________ of the population are homosexuals. (or "How could so many be wrong?")

Premise #3 – The homosexual lifestyle is a ____________________, healthy, "alternative" to heterosexuality.

We need to care that homosexuals are living a lifestyle that is physically/biologically destructive. We need to care in the same way that we would for someone who has cancer.

TALK IT OVER

1. Discuss how you feel about Chip's apology to the homosexual community. What went through your mind? Why?

2. In your opinion, what was most striking or insightful from Chip's teaching in this session?

3. How has the Church failed in its response to homosexuality? What changes need to be made?

Split families

Forgiveness
Love
Grace

Normal
↓
Healthy

4. Chip said, "Homosexuality is not something you are, it's something you do." Do you agree or disagree? Why?

5. What has been your personal attitude toward homosexuals and homosexuality? Is there any attitude that you need to repent of when it comes to your view of homosexuals?

LIVE IT OUT – B.I.O.

BIO is a word that is synonymous with "life". The key to helping you become the person God wants you to be is found in these three simple letters: B.I.O.

B = COME **"BEFORE GOD"** DAILY

Meet with Him personally through His word and prayer to enjoy His presence, receive His direction, and follow His will.

I = DO LIFE **"IN COMMUNITY"** WEEKLY

Structure your week to personally connect in safe relationships that provide love, support, transparency, challenge, and accountability.

O = BE **"ON MISSION"** 24/7

Cultivate a mindset to "live out" Jesus' love for others through acts of sacrifice and service at home, work, play, and church.

COME BEFORE GOD

The Son of Man came eating and drinking, and you say, 'Here is a glutton and a drunkard, a friend of tax collectors and "sinners."' '

LUKE 7:34 (NIV)

6. Jesus constantly risked his reputation in order to connect with people. What does this mean for us and our attitude toward those who are homosexuals?

DO LIFE IN COMMUNITY

7. Media has now normalized homosexuality. How has this impacted your family's viewing habits? As a group, talk through appropriate guidelines for your families.

BE ON MISSION

8. What specific step could you take this week to reach out in compassion to someone involved in a sinful lifestyle?

ACCELERATE *(20 minutes that turn concepts into convictions)*

Inspiration comes from hearing God's Word; motivation grows by discussing God's Word; transformation occurs when you study it for yourself.

If you want to "accelerate" your growth, here is an assignment you can do this week. To help you get the most out of this exercise, consider partnering up with somebody in your group who will also commit to do the assignment this week. Then, after you have each done the assignment, agree to spend 10 minutes by phone to share what you learned and what you are applying.

COME BEFORE GOD

1. Read the following passages carefully and slowly.

> *[35]Jesus went through all the towns and villages, teaching in their synagogues, preaching the good news of the kingdom and healing every disease and sickness. [36]When he saw the crowds, he had compassion on them, because they were harassed and helpless, like sheep without a shepherd. [37]Then he said to his disciples, "The harvest is plentiful but the workers are few. [38]Ask the Lord of the harvest, therefore, to send out workers into his harvest field."*
>
> MATTHEW 9:35-38 (NIV)

> *[27]After this, Jesus went out and saw a tax collector by the name of Levi sitting at his tax booth. "Follow me," Jesus said to him, [28]and Levi got up, left everything and followed him. [29]Then Levi held a great banquet for Jesus at his house, and a large crowd of tax*

collectors and others were eating with them. [30]But the Pharisees and the teachers of the law who belonged to their sect complained to his disciples, "Why do you eat and drink with tax collectors and 'sinners'?" [31]Jesus answered them, "It is not the healthy who need a doctor, but the sick. [32]I have not come to call the righteous, but sinners to repentance."

LUKE 5:27-32 (NIV)

2. In Matthew 9:35-38, what words or phrases describe the broken condition of people?

3. If you were to put Jesus on trial for showing compassion, what would be the evidence you could present from these 2 passages?

4. As you look at Luke 5:29, why was this a great strategy for connecting with people who didn't know God?

DO LIFE IN COMMUNITY

5. Get together with a friend this week and have a candid discussion about how we can model both "truth and grace" to those in the homosexual community.

BE ON MISSION

6. Chip said that we need to care for homosexuals in the same way that we would for someone who has cancer. Spend some time praying that God would give you a heart of compassion for those in the homosexual community.

ADDITIONAL RESOURCES

- For those discussing homosexuality with children, pre-teens and teens, read Sue Bohlin's online article: Answers to Questions Most Asked by Gay-Identifying Youth.
- For the best exegetical treatment of all Bible passages concerning homosexuality, read Daniel B. Wallace's online article: Review of Mel White's 'What the Bible Says – and Doesn't Say – About Homosexuality.'
- For a balanced, truthful, historical and loving perspective of the homosexual movement both culturally and biblically, read Kenneth Boa's online article: All That Heaven Allows: Homosexuality and the Meaning of Love.
- Log onto www.LivingOnTheEdge.org/CultureShockResources to read the articles mentioned above.

SESSION SIX

WHAT DO YOU SAY TO A GAY FRIEND?
PART 2

TAKE IT IN

REVIEW FROM SESSION 5

Premise #1 – I was born this way.

Premise #2 – 10% of the population are homosexuals. (or "How could so many be wrong?")

Premise #3 – The homosexual lifestyle is a normal, healthy, "alternative" to heterosexuality.

Premise #4 – The Bible may condemn lustful, indiscriminate homosexuality, but not ______________________, committed homosexual practice.

- Creation / Created Intent (Genesis 1:27-28, 2:18-24)
- Destruction of Sodom (Genesis 19:4-9)
- Old Testament Moral Law (Leviticus 18:21-25, 20:12-16)
- New Testament Teaching

> *[26]Because of this, God gave them over to shameful lusts. Even their women exchanged natural relations for unnatural ones.[27]In the same way the men also abandoned natural relations with women and were inflamed with lust for one another. Men committed indecent acts with other men, and received in themselves the due penalty for their perversion.*
>
> ROMANS 1:26-27 (NIV)

[9]Do you not know that the wicked will not inherit the kingdom of God? Do not be deceived: Neither the sexually immoral nor idolaters nor adulterers nor male prostitutes nor homosexual offenders [10]nor thieves nor the greedy nor drunkards nor slanderers nor swindlers will inherit the kingdom of God.

1 CORINTHIANS 6:9-10 (NIV)

Issues which make us uncomfortable!

- Why? – God's Protection, God's Provision

Premise #5 – Emotional feelings and ____________________________ to the same sex must mean I'm a homosexual.

Premise #6 – Once a homosexual, ______________________ a homosexual.

[9]Or do you not know that the unrighteous will not inherit the kingdom of God? Do not be deceived; neither fornicators, nor idolaters, nor adulterers, nor [a]effeminate, nor homosexuals, [10]nor thieves, nor the covetous, nor drunkards, nor revilers, nor swindlers, will inherit the kingdom of God. [11]Such were some of you; but you were washed, but you were sanctified, but you were justified in the name of the Lord Jesus Christ and in the Spirit of our God.

1 CORINTHIANS 6:9-11 (NASB)

Bar of Rightouness

Questions to consider:

- Would someone who has come out of a homosexual lifestyle be safe to tell you about their past and even about the fact that they still struggle?
- Are you willing to love the people who struggle with a homosexual lifestyle?
- How do we not lower the bar of righteousness and at the same time make the Church a safe place… what does that look like?

Premise #7– All Christians are ______________________________ and could never fully accept me if they knew I struggle with same sex attraction, fantasies, or practice.

TALK IT OVER

1. How do we not lower the bar of righteousness and yet create a safe place in our churches for those in the homosexual lifestyle to find the love and the grace of God?

2. As Chip was reading the passages, he asked, "How are you feeling right now? What is going through your mind?" Share with your group what you were thinking and feeling as Chip read those passages.

3. If Jesus were walking the earth today, how do you think He would respond to the controversial issue of homosexuality?

4. If someone were to come to you and tell you they want to get out of homosexuality, but they still struggle with thoughts and temptations, what would you say to them?

LIVE IT OUT – B.I.O.

BIO is a word that is synonymous with "life". The key to helping you become the person God wants you to be is found in these three simple letters: B.I.O.

B = COME "BEFORE GOD" DAILY

Meet with Him personally through His word and prayer to enjoy His presence, receive His direction, and follow His will.

I = DO LIFE "IN COMMUNITY" WEEKLY

Structure your week to personally connect in safe relationships that provide love, support, transparency, challenge, and accountability.

O = BE "ON MISSION" 24/7

Cultivate a mindset to "live out" Jesus' love for others through acts of sacrifice and service at home, work, play, and church.

Book about Broken Shell,

COME BEFORE GOD

[24]Therefore God gave them over in the sinful desires of their hearts to sexual impurity for the degrading of their bodies with one another. [25]They exchanged the truth of God for a lie, and worshiped and served created things rather than the Creator—who is forever praised. Amen. [26]Because of this, God gave them over to shameful lusts. Even their women exchanged natural relations for unnatural ones.[27]In the same way the men also abandoned natural relations with women and were inflamed with lust for one another. Men committed indecent acts with other men, and received in themselves the due penalty for their perversion.

ROMANS 1:24-27 (NIV)

5. Verse 25 says they "exchanged the truth of God for a lie." What was the truth they rejected, and what was the lie they believed?

DO LIFE IN COMMUNITY

6. What specific attitudes, words or actions displayed by Christians have alienated homosexuals? As a group, talk about ways that you can help each other be sensitive without lowering the "bar of righteousness."

BE ON MISSION

7. How could you help your church and Christian friends to have a "truth and grace" view of homosexuality?

ACCELERATE *(20 minutes that turn concepts into convictions)*

Inspiration comes from hearing God's Word; motivation grows by discussing God's Word; transformation occurs when you study it for yourself.

If you want to "accelerate" your growth, here is an assignment you can do this week. To help you get the most out of this exercise, consider partnering up with somebody in your group who will also commit to do the assignment this week. Then, after you have each done the assignment, agree to spend 10 minutes by phone to share what you learned and what you are applying.

COME BEFORE GOD

1. Read the following passage carefully and slowly.

> *[9]Do you not know that the wicked will not inherit the kingdom of God? Do not be deceived: Neither the sexually immoral nor idolaters nor adulterers nor male prostitutes nor homosexual offenders [10]nor thieves nor the greedy nor drunkards nor slanderers nor swindlers will inherit the kingdom of God. [11]And that is what some of you were. But you were washed, you were sanctified, you were justified in the name of the Lord Jesus Christ and by the Spirit of our God.*
>
> 1 CORINTHIANS 6:9-11 (NIV)

2. What does this passage teach us about the power of the Gospel to change and transform lives?

3. In verse11 Paul says that we have been "washed," "sanctified," and "justified." Write a definition of each term listed. If needed, use a commentary or Bible Study resource to help you.

DO LIFE IN COMMUNITY

4. Get together with someone from your group or a good friend this week. Share with them where you struggle with being judgmental or prejudiced. Ask your friend to speak into your life about anything they have seen or witnessed that might be prejudiced toward others.

BE ON MISSION

5. Commit to reach out to someone you know this week who might have been alienated or ostracized by Christians.

SESSION SEVEN

UNDERSTANDING ABORTION TODAY
PART 1

TAKE IT IN

Regardless of where you stand, abortion is one of the most controversial, pivotal, and emotionally charged issues of our day.

65% of women who have abortions self-identify themselves as Christians.

Framing The Issue = 2 Positions...Then and Now

- The Pro-Abortion (Pro-Choice) Position
- The Anti-Abortion (Pro-Life) Position

How Technology Transformed the Debate

Since 1973, 50 million babies have been killed in abortions.

The Issue Today = Does the pre-born baby have an inalienable right to live under any circumstances; or does the mother have the right to terminate her pregnancy to care for herself and her family's welfare?

Examining The Evidence... Thoughtfully

- From Medical Science
- From Historical Research

"This is, in all likelihood, the most important moral issue, not just of our day, but in all history."

TALK IT OVER

1. How have you seen the abortion debate change in the last 10 years? What's your perspective? What do you personally think about abortion today?

2. Chip gave the example of 16 year old Amy who went to prom and ended up pregnant. She was fearful that this would ruin her parents' reputation. What would you say to Amy and what would you say to her parents?

3. How has your church handled the abortion issue? In your opinion, what should be the Church's response and involvement?

4. Chip said, "This is in all likelihood the most important moral issue, not just of our day, but in all of history?" Do you agree with his statement? Why or why not?

LIVE IT OUT – B.I.O.

BIO is a word that is synonymous with "life". The key to helping you become the person God wants you to be is found in these three simple letters: B.I.O.

B = COME "**BEFORE GOD**" DAILY

Meet with Him personally through His word and prayer to enjoy His presence, receive His direction, and follow His will.

I = DO LIFE "**IN COMMUNITY**" WEEKLY

Structure your week to personally connect in safe relationships that provide love, support, transparency, challenge, and accountability.

O = BE "**ON MISSION**" 24/7

Cultivate a mindset to "live out" Jesus' love for others through acts of sacrifice and service at home, work, play, and church.

COME BEFORE GOD

[13]For you created my inmost being; you knit me together in my mother's womb. [14]I praise you because I am fearfully and wonderfully made; your works are wonderful, I know that full well. [15]My frame was not hidden from you when I was made in the secret place. When I was woven together in the depths of the earth, [16]your eyes saw my unformed body. All the days ordained for me were written in your book before one of them came to be.

PSALM 139:13-16 (NIV)

5. What Pro-Life statements are made in this passage? Which one most stands out to you?

DO LIFE IN COMMUNITY

6. It's probable that people in your group know someone personally who has had an abortion. There might even be someone in your group who has had that experience. Discuss what you would say to someone who has had an abortion. Give coaching and honest feedback to one another on how to appropriately approach this delicate issue.

BE ON MISSION

7. Spend some time praying together about this issue. Here are some specific items you could pray for:

    - Protection for unborn children.
    - Courage for women to choose "life."
    - Churches to preach the truth in love.
    - Churches to support those who choose to have their baby.
    - Churches to lovingly help those who have been through the trauma of an abortion.
    - Agencies on the front lines who are trying to help women choose "life."
    - Politicians who will take a stand for "life."

ACCELERATE *(20 minutes that turn concepts into convictions)*

Inspiration comes from hearing God's Word; motivation grows by discussing God's Word; transformation occurs when you study it for yourself.

If you want to "accelerate" your growth, here is an assignment you can do this week. To help you get the most out of this exercise, consider partnering up with somebody in your group who will also commit to do the assignment this week. Then, after you have each done the assignment, agree to spend 10 minutes by phone to share what you learned and what you are applying.

COME BEFORE GOD

1. Read the following passage carefully and slowly.

> *[13]For you created my inmost being; you knit me together in my mother's womb. [14]I praise you because I am fearfully and wonderfully made; your works are wonderful, I know that full well. [15]My frame was not hidden from you when I was made in the secret place. When I was woven together in the depths of the earth, [16]your eyes saw my unformed body. All the days ordained for me were written in your book before one of them came to be.*
>
> PSALM 139:13-16 (NIV)

2. Go through the passage and circle all of the words or phrases that speak of God's creative power.

3. From the passage above complete the following statement: You matter to God because…

- ______________________________
- ______________________________
- ______________________________
- ______________________________
- ______________________________
- ______________________________

DO LIFE IN COMMUNITY

4. If possible, try to have a conversation with someone who has gone through an abortion or had an unexpected pregnancy but decided to have the baby. Try to gain insight into their personal journey and ask them how the body of Christ could have helped to support them.

BE ON MISSION

5. Contact a local crisis pregnancy agency to let them know that you appreciate their ministry. Then ask them what kind of help they could use. Commit to helping them by either making a donation, volunteering some time, or providing for a need they have.

ADDITIONAL RESOURCES

- Log onto www.LivingOnTheEdge.org/CultureShockResources to watch video testimonies from women whose lives have been affected by abortion.

SESSION EIGHT

UNDERSTANDING ABORTION TODAY
PART 2

CULTURE SHOCK

TAKE IT IN

Examining The Evidence...

- From the Biblical record

Premise #1 – All life is sacred. Human life is the most valuable and precious commodity in the world.

- Value by Creation and Design

> *So God created man in his own image, in the image of God he created him; male and female he created them.*
>
> GENESIS 1:27 (NIV)

- Value by Protection Afforded

> *Whoever sheds the blood of man, by man shall his blood be shed; for in the image of God has God made man.*
>
> GENESIS 9:6 (ESV)

- Value by Cost

> *You were bought at a price. Therefore honor God with your body.*
>
> 1 CORINTHIANS 6:20 (NIV)

For even the Son of man came not to be ministered unto, but to minister, and to give his life a ransom for many.

MARK 10:45

Premise #2 – Scripture affords the same sacred value on the fetus/pre-born baby as it does all other human life.

- Value by Design

[13]For you created my inmost being; you knit me together in my mother's womb. [14]I praise you because I am fearfully and wonderfully made; your works are wonderful, I know that full well.[15]My frame was not hidden from you when I was made in the secret place. When I was woven together in the depths of the earth, [16]your eyes saw my unformed body. All the days ordained for me were written in your book before one of them came to be.

PSALM 139:13-16 (NIV)

"Before I formed you in the womb I knew you, before you were born I set you apart; I appointed you as a prophet to the nations. "

JEREMIAH 1:5 (NIV)

- Value by Protection Afforded

> *[22]If men who are fighting hit a pregnant woman and she gives birth prematurely but there is no serious injury, the offender must be fined whatever the woman's husband demands and the court allows. [23]But if there is serious injury, you are to take life for life, [24]eye for eye, tooth for tooth, hand for hand, foot for foot, [25]burn for burn, wound for wound, bruise for bruise.*
>
> EXODUS 21:22-25 (NIV)

- Value by Cost

> *Surely I was sinful at birth, sinful from the time my mother conceived me.*
>
> PSALM 51:5 (NIV)

- Warnings from Personal Experience
    - The Pro-Abortion Camp
    - The Pro-Life Camp

Application: Responding To Abortion Today

- Find ______________________________ and ______________________.

[5]You are forgiving and good, O Lord, abounding in love to all who call to you. [6]Hear my prayer, O LORD; listen to my cry for mercy. [7]In the day of my trouble I will call to you, for you will answer me.

PSALM 86:5-7 (NIV)

If we confess our sins, he is faithful and just and will forgive us our sins and purify us from all unrighteousness.

1 JOHN 1:9 (NIV)

- Take ______________________________.

[11]Rescue those being led away to death; hold back those staggering toward slaughter. [12]If you say, "But we knew nothing about this," does not he who weighs the heart perceive it? Does not he who guards your life know it? Will he not repay each person according to what he has done?

PROVERBS 24:11-12 (NIV)

Abortion isn't political, it's moral.

- Setting ________________________________. (Romans 13:1-7)
- Acting in ________________________________. (Ephesians 4:15-18)

Our methods and message must tell the same story.

TALK IT OVER

1. Which of the four applications that Chip shared do you feel most passionate to take the next step with?

2. How would you "lovingly" articulate your convictions if someone asked you what you believed concerning abortion? How would you support your position?

3. What was most helpful and insightful from Chip's teaching in this session?

4. Chip said that our methods must match our message. What are appropriate ways for Christians to get involved and voice their concerns?

LIVE IT OUT – B.I.O.

BIO is a word that is synonymous with "life". The key to helping you become the person God wants you to be is found in these three simple letters: B.I.O.

B = COME **"BEFORE GOD"** DAILY

Meet with Him personally through His word and prayer to enjoy His presence, receive His direction, and follow His will.

I = DO LIFE **"IN COMMUNITY"** WEEKLY

Structure your week to personally connect in safe relationships that provide love, support, transparency, challenge, and accountability.

O = BE **"ON MISSION"** 24/7

Cultivate a mindset to "live out" Jesus' love for others through acts of sacrifice and service at home, work, play, and church.

COME BEFORE GOD

Then God said, "Let us make man in our image, in our likeness, and let them rule over the fish of the sea and the birds of the air, over the livestock, over all the earth, and over all the creatures that move along the ground." So God created man in his own image, in the image of God he created him; male and female he created them.

GENESIS 1:26-27 (NIV)

5. If someone told you they were considering an abortion, what could you say to them out of this passage? What else would you say to them?

DO LIFE IN COMMUNITY

6. Chip said the Bible is full of people who God loved deeply but who made big mistakes. God forgave them, cleansed them and used them. When someone in the group falls into sin, what can the group do that will help bring healing and help? If you were the one who had fallen into sin, what would you expect and want from the group?

BE ON MISSION

7. As you look at the gifts and talents in your group, how could you as a group be a support to someone with an unexpected pregnancy?

As a group, take the challenge to support a young woman with an unexpected pregnancy. If you don't know of someone personally, contact a crisis pregnancy center.

ACCELERATE *(20 minutes that turn concepts into convictions)*

Inspiration comes from hearing God's Word; motivation grows by discussing God's Word; transformation occurs when you study it for yourself.

If you want to "accelerate" your growth, here is an assignment you can do this week. To help you get the most out of this exercise, consider partnering up with somebody in your group who will also commit to do the assignment this week. Then, after you have each done the assignment, agree to spend 10 minutes by phone to share what you learned and what you are applying.

COME BEFORE GOD

1. Read the following passage carefully and slowly.

[26]Then God said, "Let us make man in our image, in our likeness, and let them rule over the fish of the sea and the birds of the air, over the livestock, over all the earth, and over all the creatures that move along the ground." [27]So God created man in his own image, in

the image of God he created him; male and female he created them. [28]*God blessed them and said to them, "Be fruitful and increase in number; fill the earth and subdue it. Rule over the fish of the sea and the birds of the air and over every living creature that moves on the ground."*

GENESIS 1:26-28 (NIV)

2. What words or phrases in this passage speak of the high value of human beings?

3. What does it mean that God created us in His image?

DO LIFE IN COMMUNITY

4. Select someone from your group and write them a letter or e-mail this week. Let them know you value them and share the ways you see the image of God in them.

BE ON MISSION

5. If you are a parent, sit down with your kids this week and talk to them about the sanctity of life. Read Genesis 1:26-28 and Psalm 139:13-16. If you don't have kids, consider doing this with a nephew or niece.

SESSION NINE

THE CHURCH AND THE ENVIRONMENT
PART 1

TAKE IT IN

What do you think?

- The real issue with the environment is whether global warming is happening or not.
- "Tree huggers" and environmentalists are liberal or new age folks seeking to thwart economic progress and prosperity.
- The problem we are in today is a direct result of the "dominion" dogma, taught for centuries from Genesis chapter 1.
- The whole environmental debate is overblown. The Bible says it's all going to burn up anyway.
- The earth is our "Sacred Mother" and the equal giver of life to all species, and as such, all must be protected.
- The "going green" movement in business and government is just a sham to exercise undue control and increase profits.

The Question: How are followers of Christ to think, act and respond to the controversial issue of the environment?

1. The earth ______________________________ to God.

> *[1]The earth is the LORD's, and everything in it, the world, and all who live in it; [2]for he founded it on the seas and established it on the waters.*
>
> PSALM 24:1-2 (NIV)

Implication = We are to honor God's creation.

In the beginning God created the heavens and the earth.

GENESIS 1:1 (NIV)

The earth is valuable, precious, irreplaceable and ______________________________.

2. God appointed mankind ______________________________________ over the earth.

[16]The highest heavens belong to the LORD, but the earth he has given to man.

PSALM 115:16 (NIV)

Implication = We are the earth's Vice Regents.

God blessed them and said to them, "Be fruitful and increase in number; fill the earth and subdue it. Rule over the fish in the sea and the birds in the sky and over every living creature that moves on the ground."

GENESIS 1:28 (NIV)

The LORD God took the man and put him in the Garden of Eden to work it and take care of it.

GENESIS 2:15 (NIV)

3. The earth/nature has intrinsic value and reflects the ______________________

______________________________________ of the Creator.

[1]The heavens declare the glory of God; the skies proclaim the work of his hands. [2]Day after day they pour forth speech; night after night they reveal knowledge.

PSALM 19:1-2 (NIV)

Implication = We must explore not exploit, enjoy not worship the earth.

People who begin to worship the creation pretty soon lose sight of the

______________________________.

[19]Since what may be known about God is plain to them, because God has made it plain to them. [20]For since the creation of the world God's invisible qualities—his eternal power and divine nature—have been clearly seen, being understood from what has been made, so that people are without excuse. [21]For although they knew God, they neither glorified him as God nor gave thanks to him, but their thinking became futile and their foolish hearts were darkened.

ROMANS 1:19-21 (NIV)

TALK IT OVER

1. Share a specific time when you interacted with nature in a way that your heart resonated — where there was a sense of the presence of God.

2. How would you characterize your awareness of and involvement in environmental issues?

3. Why do you think the Church has been so silent on the environment?

4. What new insight did you gain from either Chip's teaching or the Scripture passages he read?

5. Chip said that God gave mankind "dominion" over the earth. In practical terms, what does it mean for us to have "dominion" over the earth? How has that been violated or abused?

LIVE IT OUT – B.I.O.

BIO is a word that is synonymous with "life". The key to helping you become the person God wants you to be is found in these three simple letters: B.I.O.

B = COME **"BEFORE GOD"** DAILY

Meet with Him personally through His word and prayer to enjoy His presence, receive His direction, and follow His will.

I = DO LIFE **"IN COMMUNITY"** WEEKLY

Structure your week to personally connect in safe relationships that provide love, support, transparency, challenge, and accountability.

O = BE **"ON MISSION"** 24/7

Cultivate a mindset to "live out" Jesus' love for others through acts of sacrifice and service at home, work, play, and church.

COME BEFORE GOD

> *[1]The heavens declare the glory of God; the skies proclaim the work of his hands. [2]Day after day they pour forth speech; night after night they display knowledge. [3]There is no speech or language where their voice is not heard.*
>
> PSALM19:1-3 (NIV)

6. What lessons do we learn about God's character and God's ways as we observe His creation? (i.e.: The seasons teach us that God is in the business of renewing life.)

DO LIFE IN COMMUNITY

7. Chip challenged us to "explore not exploit" God's creation. What could you do together as a group in the next month to explore some of God's glorious creation?

BE ON MISSION

8. In light of this teaching, what adjustments do you need to make personally and how can this group provide support and accountability?

ACCELERATE *(20 minutes that turn concepts into convictions)*

Inspiration comes from hearing God's Word; motivation grows by discussing God's Word; transformation occurs when you study it for yourself.

If you want to "accelerate" your growth, here is an assignment you can do this week. To help you get the most out of this exercise, consider partnering up with somebody in your group who will also commit to do the assignment this week. Then, after you have each done the assignment, agree to spend 10 minutes by phone to share what you learned and what you are applying.

COME BEFORE GOD

1. Read the following passage carefully and slowly.

[1]Let all that I am praise the LORD. O LORD my God, how great you are! You are robed with honor and majesty. [2]You are dressed in a robe of light. You stretch out the starry curtain of the heavens; [3]you lay out the rafters of your home in the rain clouds. You make the clouds your chariot; you ride upon the wings of the wind. [4]The winds are your messengers; flames of fire are your servants. [5]You placed the world on its foundation so it would never be moved. [6]You clothed the earth with floods of water, water that covered even the mountains. [7]At your command, the water fled; at the sound of your thunder, it hurried away. [8]Mountains rose and valleys sank to the levels you decreed. [9]Then you set a firm boundary for the seas, so they would never again cover the earth. [10]You make springs pour water into the ravines, so streams gush down from the mountains. [11]They provide water for all the animals, and the wild donkeys quench their thirst. [12]The birds nest beside the streams and sing among the branches of the trees. [13]You send rain on the mountains from your heavenly home, and you fill the earth with the fruit of your labor. [14]You cause grass to grow for the livestock and plants for people to use. You allow them to produce food from the earth — [15]wine to make them glad, olive oil to soothe their skin, and bread to give them strength. [16]The trees of the LORD are well cared for — the cedars of Lebanon that he planted. [17]There the birds make their nests, and the storks make their homes in the cypresses. [18]High in the mountains live the wild goats, and the rocks form a refuge for the hyraxes.

PSALM 104:1-18 (NLT)

2. What do verses 1-9 teach us about God's relationship to creation?

3. How is God's relationship to creation in verses 1-9 pictured differently in verses 10-18?

4. What new insight about God or creation did you learn from this passage?

DO LIFE IN COMMUNITY

5. Plan an outing with a family member or friend where you can get out and explore and enjoy God's creation.

BE ON MISSION

6. Have a conversation with your family or a friend about God's creation. Come up with some clear action steps that each of you can take to start being a better steward of our planet.

SESSION TEN

THE CHURCH AND THE ENVIRONMENT
PART 2

CULTURE SHOCK

TAKE IT IN

REVIEW FROM SESSION 9

1. *The earth belongs to God.*
2. *God appointed mankind "dominion" over the earth.*
3. *The earth/nature has intrinsic value and reflects the character and beauty of the Creator.*

4. Mankind is placed in the middle of the created hierarchy and is

   __________________ __________________

   to God (above) and for the animals, plants and resources (below).

> *[3]When I consider your heavens, the work of your fingers, the moon and the stars, which you have set in place, [4]what is mankind that you are mindful of them, human beings that you care for them? [5]You have made them a little lower than the angels and crowned them with glory and honor. [6]You made them rulers over the works of your hands; you put everything under their feet: [7]all flocks and herds, and the animals of the wild, [8]the birds in the sky, and the fish in the sea, all that swim the paths of the seas.*
>
> PSALM 8:3-8 (NIV)

All living things have value, but not all living things have equal value.

Implication = We are to use, not abuse animals, plants, and resources to glorify God.

5. God commands environmental stewardship to __________________ the land, animals and vegetation for the common good. (Leviticus 25:1-12, 23; Deuteronomy 20:19-20; 25:4; Matthew 6:26)

Implication = Consumption and productivity must be governed by the boundaries of conservation.

6. Christ's ________________________________ work includes the earth.

[19]For the creation waits in eager expectation for the children of God to be revealed. [20]For the creation was subjected to frustration, not by its own choice, but by the will of the one who subjected it, in hope [21]that the creation itself will be liberated from its bondage to decay and brought into the freedom and glory of the children of God.

ROMANS 8:19-21 (NIV)

Implication = We must treat the earth with the same priority God does.

[1]Then I saw a new heaven and a new earth, for the first heaven and the first earth had passed away, and there was no longer any sea. [2]I saw the Holy City, the new Jerusalem, coming down out of heaven from God, prepared as a bride beautifully dressed for her husband. [3]And I heard a loud voice from the throne saying, "Now the dwelling of God is with men, and he will live with them. They will be his people, and God himself will be with them and be their God. [4]He will wipe every tear from their eyes. There will be no more death or mourning or crying or pain, for the old order of things has passed away." [5]He who was seated on the throne said, "I am making everything new!"

REVELATION 21:1-5A (NIV)

The most conscientious stewards of the earth should be the followers of Jesus.

WHERE DO WE GO FROM HERE?

- Recognize and focus on the verifiable issues we can all agree upon.
    - Clean air
    - Clean water
    - Balanced land use
    - Preserving the beauty
    - Productivity and progress with constraints for conservation
    - Eliminate waste
    - Limit non-biodegradable plastics
    - Recycle

- Identify the three root causes of our poor environmental stewardship.
    1. Greed
    2. Ignorance
    3. Carelessness

Redeeming Cans + Bottles

- Practical steps for you and your friends/family:
    1. ______________________________
    2. ______________________________
    3. ______________________________
    4. ______________________________

TALK IT OVER

1. Which of Chip's four practical steps of Explore, Educate, Engage or Empower are you actually going to do?

2. Share one of your most moving encounters and experiences you've ever had with God's creation.

3. Read Psalm 8:3-8. In light of the topic for this session, what most stands out to you in the passage? Why?

4. Chip said consumption and productivity must be governed by the boundaries of conservation. How environmentally aware and friendly is your local community or city?

LIVE IT OUT – B.I.O.

BIO is a word that is synonymous with "life". The key to helping you become the person God wants you to be is found in these three simple letters: B.I.O.

B = COME "**BEFORE GOD**" DAILY

Meet with Him personally through His word and prayer to enjoy His presence, receive His direction, and follow His will.

I = DO LIFE "**IN COMMUNITY**" WEEKLY

Structure your week to personally connect in safe relationships that provide love, support, transparency, challenge, and accountability.

O = BE "**ON MISSION**" 24/7

Cultivate a mindset to "live out" Jesus' love for others through acts of sacrifice and service at home, work, play, and church.

COME BEFORE GOD

[19]For the creation waits in eager expectation for the children of God to be revealed. [20]For the creation was subjected to frustration, not by its own choice, but by the will of the one who subjected it, in hope [21]that the creation itself will be liberated from its bondage to decay and brought into the freedom and glory of the children of God.

ROMANS 8:19-21 (NIV)

5. What does it mean that "creation was subjected to frustration?" And, what does it mean that "creation itself will be liberated from its bondage to decay and brought into the freedom and glory of the children of God?"

DO LIFE IN COMMUNITY

6. Decide on one action (i.e.: stop using plastic water bottles) everyone in your group will commit to practice.

BE ON MISSION

7. How could you build bridges with those who are non-believers but are passionate about the environment?

ACCELERATE *(20 minutes that turn concepts into convictions)*

Inspiration comes from hearing God's Word; motivation grows by discussing God's Word; transformation occurs when you study it for yourself.

If you want to "accelerate" your growth, here is an assignment you can do this week. To help you get the most out of this exercise, consider partnering up with somebody in your group who will also commit to do the assignment this week. Then, after you have each done the assignment, agree to spend 10 minutes by phone to share what you learned and what you are applying.

COME BEFORE GOD

1. Read the following passage carefully and slowly.

> *[19]You made the moon to mark the seasons, and the sun knows when to set. [20]You send the darkness, and it becomes night, when all the forest animals prowl about. [21]Then the young lions roar for their prey, stalking the food provided by God. [22]At dawn they slink back into their dens to rest. [23]Then people go off to their work, where they labor until evening. [24]O LORD, what a variety of things you have made! In wisdom you have made them all. The earth is full of your creatures. [25]Here is the ocean, vast and wide, teeming with life of every kind, both large and small. [26]See the ships sailing along, and Leviathan, which you made to play in the sea. [27]They all depend on you to give them food as they need it. [28]When you supply it, they gather it. You open your hand to feed them, and they are richly satisfied. [29]But if you turn away from them, they panic. When you take away their breath, they die and turn again to dust. [30]When you give them your breath, life is created, and you renew the face of the earth. [31]May the glory of the LORD continue forever! The LORD takes pleasure in all he has made!*

PSALM 104:19-31 (NLT)

2. From this passage, list your observations about God's creative work.

- ______________________________
- ______________________________
- ______________________________
- ______________________________
- ______________________________
- ______________________________

3. Circle the phrases that speak of God's provision and care for man.

4. What are the implications of verse 31 for how we should steward creation?

DO LIFE IN COMMUNITY

5. Schedule a 10-minute phone call with a friend to share what you've learned from these sessions on the environment.

BE ON MISSION

6. As you go through everyday life this week, make it a point to pay attention to God's creation. As you pay attention this week, let your encounter with creation become an opportunity to praise and thank God.

SESSION ELEVEN

THE CHURCH AND POLITICS
PART 1

TAKE IT IN

How can you say you love God and...

Yet talk about political issues in church?

- **The Position** = Any subject or issue that is directly political or has political overtones should never be talked about in church.

- **The Presuppositions** =

    - Sacred vs. secular mentality (faith is a personal issue)
    - Pluralistic vs. Pluralism
    - Functional Separatism

Yet not take a stand on political issues in church?

- **The Position** = The Church is a tool in the hands of God to turn a secular culture back to God.

- **The Presuppositions** =

    - America has a covenant relationship with God (much like Israel).
    - Moral and cultural change is the primary mandate of the Church and is accomplished through the political process
    - The Church (gathered) and individual believers (Church scattered) have the same calling

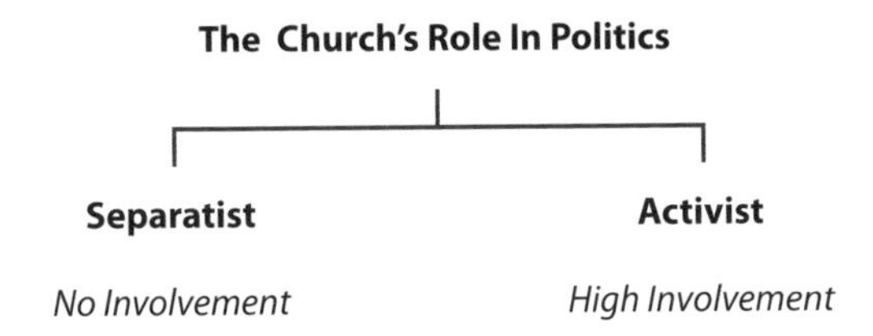

The Question = How to navigate through the maze of the Church/Politics conflict?

The Answer = Four Biblical Absolutes

Building a Theological Framework to Think Clearly About the Church and Politics

1. There are two kingdoms in ____________________. *(John 18:36-37, 19:10-12)*
2. Every believer has dual ____________________. *(Mark 12:13-17)*
3. Human governments are ordained by God to ____________________ evil. *(Romans 13:1-7)*
4. The church is ordained by God to make disciples. *(Matthew 28:18-20)*

TALK IT OVER

1. Chip said, "The government has the power to restrain evil, but government does not have the power to create righteousness in people's hearts." If that's true, how should that change the way Christians approach "Church and Politics?"

____

____

____

#3 Overthrow of an evil government?

2. Some would say that America has a "covenant" relationship with God much like Israel had in the Old Testament. What would you say to that? What biblical teaching would you give to support your position?

But our citizenship is in heaven. And we eagerly await a Savior from there, the Lord Jesus Christ.

PHILIPPIANS 3:20 (NIV)

3. If you actually lived as a citizen of heaven, what would change in your life?

4. How should being a citizen of heaven shape your view of politics? How should being a citizen of heaven impact your citizenship as an American?

LIVE IT OUT – B.I.O.

BIO is a word that is synonymous with "life". The key to helping you become the person God wants you to be is found in these three simple letters: B.I.O.

B = COME **"BEFORE GOD"** DAILY

Meet with Him personally through His word and prayer to enjoy His presence, receive His direction, and follow His will.

I = DO LIFE **"IN COMMUNITY"** WEEKLY

Structure your week to personally connect in safe relationships that provide love, support, transparency, challenge, and accountability.

O = BE **"ON MISSION"** 24/7

Cultivate a mindset to "live out" Jesus' love for others through acts of sacrifice and service at home, work, play, and church.

COME BEFORE GOD

5. Read Romans 13:1-7. What stands out to you from this passage? Why?
   Is there anything in this passage that challenges your view of Church and Politics?

DO LIFE IN COMMUNITY

6. Chip said that when the Church makes disciples, the culture will be transformed as Christians begin to live like Christians. What could you do as a small group to engage the culture and show the love of Christ?

BE ON MISSION

7. How can being a "good citizen" help with the spread of the gospel? As you think about your everyday life, what are some practical ways you could build bridges for the Gospel by being a good citizen?

Just voting (?) makes a good citizen.

ACCELERATE *(20 minutes that turn concepts into convictions)*

Inspiration comes from hearing God's Word; motivation grows by discussing God's Word; transformation occurs when you study it for yourself.

If you want to "accelerate" your growth, here is an assignment you can do this week. To help you get the most out of this exercise, consider partnering up with somebody in your group who will also commit to do the assignment this week. Then, after you have each done the assignment, agree to spend 10 minutes by phone to share what you learned and what you are applying.

COME BEFORE GOD

1. Read the following passage carefully and slowly.

> *[1]Everyone must submit himself to the governing authorities, for there is no authority except that which God has established. The authorities that exist have been established by God. [2]Consequently, he who rebels against the authority is rebelling against what God has instituted, and those who do so will bring judgment on themselves. [3]For rulers hold no terror for those who do right, but for those who do wrong. Do you want to be free from fear of the one in authority? Then do what is right and he will commend you. [4]For he is God's servant to do you good. But if you do wrong, be afraid, for he does not bear the sword for nothing. He is God's servant, an agent of wrath to bring punishment on the wrongdoer. [5]Therefore, it is necessary to submit to the authorities, not only because of possible punishment but also because of conscience. [6]This is also why you pay taxes, for the authorities are God's servants, who give their full time to governing. [7]Give everyone what you owe him: If you owe taxes, pay taxes; if revenue, then revenue; if respect, then respect; if honor, then honor.*
>
> ROMANS 13:1-7 (NIV)

2. Go through the passage and make a list of all the purposes for which God established government.

3. Go through the passage again and circle all of the phrases that describe our responsibility to government.

4. Go through the passage one more time and underline all the phrases referring to government as God's instrument.

5. What does Paul mean when he says we should submit to the authorities "not only because of possible punishment but also because of conscience?"

DO LIFE IN COMMUNITY

6. Get together with a friend this week and have a time of prayer for those serving in government. (Don't forget to pray for local officials including: police officers, fire fighters, judges and city council members.)

BE ON MISSION

7. Romans 13:7 says we should give people what is owed them.

if respect, then respect; if honor, then honor.

ROMANS 13:7 (NIV)

This week, commit to doing something that would demonstrate respect and honor for a government official. You could write a card, send an e-mail or express appreciation in person.

SESSION TWELVE

THE CHURCH AND POLITICS
PART 2

CULTURE SHOCK

TAKE IT IN

The Next Question = How do we move from a theological framework to specific applications for daily living?

The Answer = Three Biblical Principles

Understanding the Roles and Responsibilities of the Church, the Government, and the Individual Believer in the Political Arena

1. Let the Church be the ____________________!

2. Don't expect the ____________________ to achieve what only the Church can accomplish!

3. Don't expect the Church to accomplish what only ____________________ can achieve!

Application

- A Word to Separatists
- A Word to Activists

TALK IT OVER

1. What is your biggest takeaway from the two sessions on Church and Politics?

2. When it comes to politics, how did this lesson help you better understand the role of government? The Church? Individual believers?

3. The first principle Chip mentioned was "to let the Church be the Church." When it comes to politics, when does the Church lose sight of it's purpose and become inappropriately involved in politics?

4. Chuck Colson has said, "The danger with Christian political movements per se is that they tend to make the Gospel hostage to particular political agendas." What does he mean by that statement? How can we keep from falling into this danger?

You are the salt
You are the light
You are the Leaven

LIVE IT OUT – B.I.O.

BIO is a word that is synonymous with "life". The key to helping you become the person God wants you to be is found in these three simple letters: B.I.O.

B = COME **"BEFORE GOD"** DAILY

Meet with Him personally through His word and prayer to enjoy His presence, receive His direction, and follow His will.

I = DO LIFE **"IN COMMUNITY"** WEEKLY

Structure your week to personally connect in safe relationships that provide love, support, transparency, challenge, and accountability.

O = BE **"ON MISSION"** 24/7

Cultivate a mindset to "live out" Jesus' love for others through acts of sacrifice and service at home, work, play, and church.

COME BEFORE GOD

I urge, then, first of all, that requests, prayers, intercession and thanksgiving be made for everyone — for kings and all those in authority, that we may live peaceful and quiet lives in all godliness and holiness. This is good, and pleases God our Savior who wants all men to be saved and to come to a knowledge of the truth.

1 TIMOTHY 2:1-4 (NIV)

5. What stands out to you from this passage? How can you put this passage into action?

DO LIFE IN COMMUNITY

6. As a group, take a few minutes to put 1 Timothy 2:1 into practice right now. Have a dedicated time of prayer for government officials.

BE ON MISSION

7. Chip said that many of us want somebody else (Government or Church) to accomplish what God says is our job. As an individual believer, how can you do a better job of being "salt and light?"

ACCELERATE *(20 minutes that turn concepts into convictions)*

Inspiration comes from hearing God's Word; motivation grows by discussing God's Word; transformation occurs when you study it for yourself.

If you want to "accelerate" your growth, here is an assignment you can do this week. To help you get the most out of this exercise, consider partnering up with somebody in your group who will also commit to do the assignment this week. Then, after you have each done the assignment, agree to spend 10 minutes by phone to share what you learned and what you are applying.

COME BEFORE GOD

1. Read the following passages carefully and slowly.

> *[42]They devoted themselves to the apostles' teaching and to the fellowship, to the breaking of bread and to prayer. [43]Everyone was filled with awe, and many wonders and miraculous signs were done by the apostles. [44]All the believers were together and had everything in common. [45]Selling their possessions and goods, they gave to anyone as he had need. [46]Every day they continued to meet together in the temple courts. They broke bread in their homes and ate together with glad and sincere hearts, [47]praising God and enjoying the favor of all the people. And the Lord added to their number daily those who were being saved.*
>
> ACTS 2:42-47 (NIV)

[32]All the believers were one in heart and mind. No one claimed that any of his possessions was his own, but they shared everything they had. [33]With great power the apostles continued to testify to the resurrection of the Lord Jesus, and much grace was upon them all. [34]There were no needy persons among them. For from time to time those who owned lands or houses sold them, brought the money from the sales [35]and put it at the apostles' feet, and it was distributed to anyone as he had need.

ACTS 4:32-25 (NIV)

2. Go through these two passages and circle all of the action verbs.

3. What are some of the things the Early Church did that would have been a powerful testimony to unbelievers?

4. What does it mean in Acts 4:32 that "all the believers were one in heart and mind"? What is the difference between unity and uniformity?

DO LIFE IN COMMUNITY

Get together with a friend this week or schedule a time to talk by phone. First, read Acts 2:42-47 and then discuss the following questions.

5. What characteristic of the Early Church are you most drawn to in this passage? Why?

6. What gets in the way of the Church today living like the early church in Acts 2?

7. Part of what gave the Early Church such power was that they lived in authentic community with one another. What steps do you need to take to live in true, authentic community?

BE ON MISSION

8. One of the prominent characteristics of the Early Church was that they shared what they had and met the needs of others. Decide today to share what you have and meet a need of someone you know.

SMALL GROUP
LEADER RESOURCES

CULTURE
SHOCK

GROUP AGREEMENT

People come to groups with a variety of expectations. The purpose of a group agreement is simply to make sure everyone is on the same page and that we have some common expectations.

The following Group Agreement is a tool to help you discuss specific guidelines during your first meeting. Modify anything that does not work for your group, then be sure to discuss the questions in the section called Our Game Plan. This will help you to have an even greater group experience!

WE AGREE TO THE FOLLOWING PRIORITIES

- **Take the Bible Seriously** — Seek to understand and apply God's truth in the Bible.
- **Group Attendance** — Give priority to the group meeting (call if I am going to be absent or late).
- **Safe Environment** — Create a safe place where people can be heard and feel loved (no snap judgments or simple fixes).
- **Respectful Discussion** — Speak in a respectful and honoring way to our mate and others in the group.
- **Be Confidential** — Keep anything that is shared strictly confidential and within the group.
- **Spiritual Health** — Give group members permission to help me live a godly, healthy spiritual life that is pleasing to God.
- **Building Relationships** — Get to know the other members of the group and pray for them regularly.
- **Pursue B.I.O.** — Encourage and challenge each other in coming "**B**efore God," doing life together "**I**n Community" and being "**O**n Mission 24/7."
- **Prayer** — Regularly pray with and for each other.
- **Other**

OUR GAME PLAN

1. What day and time will we meet?

2. Where will we meet?

3. How long will we meet each week?

4. What will we do for refreshments?

5. What will we do about childcare?

LEADER NOTES

As an additional resource to help you in leading your group, we have prepared brief coaching videos. These 3-minute videos can be found online at www.LivingOnTheEdge.org/CultureShockCoaching.

HOW TO MAKE THIS A MEANINGFUL GROUP EXPERIENCE

BEFORE THE GROUP ARRIVES

1. **Be prepared.** Your personal preparation can make a huge difference in the quality of the group experience. We strongly suggest previewing both the DVD teaching by Chip Ingram and the study guide.

2. **Pray for your group members by name.** Ask God to use your time together to touch the heart of every person in your group. Expect God to challenge and change people as a result of this study.

3. **Provide refreshments.** There's nothing like food to help a group relax and connect with each other. For the first week, we suggest you prepare a snack, but after that, ask other group members to bring the food so that they share in the responsibilities of the group and make a commitment to return.

4. **Relax.** Don't try to imitate someone else's style of leading a group. Lead the group in a way that fits your style and temperament. Remember that people may feel nervous showing up for a small group study, so put them at ease when they arrive. Make sure to have all the details covered prior to your group meeting, so that once people start arriving, you can focus on them.

TAKE IT IN

1. **Get the video ready.** Each video session on the DVD will have 3 components. The first couple of minutes Chip will introduce this week's topic Then, you will watch the actual teaching content that Chip taught in front of a live audience. This portion of the video will be roughly 25 minutes in length. Finally, Chip will then share some closing thoughts and set up the discussion time for your group.

2. **Have ample materials.** Before you start the video, make sure everyone has their own copy of the study guide. Encourage the group to follow along in their study guides, as the outline provides an opportunity to fill in the blanks and take notes.

3. **Arrange the room.** Set up the chairs in the room so that everyone can see the television. Arrange the room in such a way that it is conducive to discussion.

TALK IT OVER

Here are some guidelines for leading the discussion time:

1. **Make this a discussion, not a lecture.** Resist the temptation to do all the talking, and to answer your own questions. Don't be afraid of a few moments of silence while people formulate their answers.

   Don't feel like you need to have all the answers. There is nothing wrong with simply saying, "I don't know the answer to that, but I'll see if I can find an answer this week."

2. **Encourage everyone to participate.** Don't let one person dominate, but also don't pressure quieter members to speak during the first couple of sessions. Be patient. Ask good follow up questions and be sensitive to delicate issues.

3. **Affirm people's participation and input.** If an answer is clearly wrong, ask "What led you to that conclusion?" or ask what the rest of the group thinks. If a disagreement arises, don't be too quick to shut it down! The discussion can draw out important perspectives, and if you can't resolve it there, offer to research it further and return to the issue next week.

   However, if someone goes on the offensive and engages in personal attack, you will need to step in as the leader. In the midst of spirited discussion, we must also remember that people are fragile and there is no place for disrespect.

4. **Detour when necessary.** If an important question is raised that is not in the study guide, take time to discuss it. Also, if someone shares something personal and emotional, take time for them. Stop and pray for them right then. Allow the Holy Spirit room to maneuver, and follow His prompting when the discussion changes direction.

5. **Subgroup.** One of the principles of small group life is "when numbers go up, sharing goes down." So, if you have a large group, sometimes you may want to split up into groups of 4-6 for the discussion time. This is a great way to give everyone, even the quieter members, a chance to share. Choose someone in the group to guide each of the smaller groups through the discussion. This involves others in the leadership of the group, and provides an opportunity for training new leaders.

6. **Prayer.** Be sensitive to the fact that some people in your group may be uncomfortable praying out loud. As a general rule, don't call on people to pray unless you have asked them ahead of time or have heard them pray in public. But this can also be a time to help people build their confidence to pray in a group. Consider having prayer times that ask people to just say a word or sentence of thanks to God.

LIVE IT OUT

BIO is a word that is synonymous with "life". The key to helping you become the person God wants you to be is found in these three simple letters: B.I.O.

B = COME "**BEFORE GOD**" DAILY

Meet with Him personally through His word and prayer to enjoy His presence, receive His direction, and follow His will.

I = DO LIFE "**IN COMMUNITY**" WEEKLY

Structure your week to personally connect in safe relationships that provide love, support, transparency, challenge, and accountability.

O = BE "**ON MISSION**" 24/7

Cultivate a mindset to "live out" Jesus' love for others through acts of sacrifice and service at home, work, play, and church.

ACCELERATE *(20 minutes that turn concepts into convictions)*

Inspiration comes from hearing God's Word; motivation grows by discussing God's Word; transformation occurs when you study it for yourself.

If you want to "accelerate" your growth, here is an assignment you can do this week. To help you get the most out of this exercise, consider partnering up with somebody in your group who will also commit to do the assignment this week. Then, after you have each done the assignment, agree to spend 10 minutes by phone to share what you learned and what you are applying.

SESSION NOTES

Thanks for hosting this series on controversial issues. This compelling series will equip you with a biblical view of these issues and help you know how to communicate them. Whether you are brand new at leading a small group or you are a seasoned veteran, God is going to use you. God has a long history of using ordinary people to get His work done.

These brief notes are intended to help prepare you for each week's session. By spending just a few minutes each week previewing the video and going over these session notes you will set the table for a great group experience. Also, don't forget to pray for your group each week.

SESSION 1: Whatever Happened to Right & Wrong? (Part 1)

- If your group doesn't know each other well, be sure that you spend some time getting acquainted. Don't rush right into the video lesson. Remember, small groups are not just about a study or a meeting, they are about relationships.
- Be sure to capture everyone's contact information. At the back of your study guide, you will find a roster where each member can note everyone's names and contact information.
- When you are ready to start the session, be sure that each person in your group has a copy of the study guide. The small group study guide is important for people to follow along and to take notes.

- Spend a little time in this first session talking about B.I.O. These 3 core practices are the pathway to maturity. You will see these letters and terms throughout this curriculum. Start getting your group comfortable with the concepts of coming before God daily, doing life together in community weekly, and being on mission 24/7.
- Lead by example. Sometimes Chip will ask you as the facilitator to lead the way by answering the first question. This allows you to lead by example and your willingness to share openly about your life will help others feel the permission to do the same.
- Before you wrap up your group time, be sure to introduce the Accelerate exercise in the study guide. This is an assignment everyone can do during the week that will help turbo charge their growth. Encourage them to find a partner in the group who they can talk to each week about the Accelerate exercise.
- It would be a good idea to review the discussion questions for this week's session. In most weeks, there are 7 discussion questions. If that is too many for your group to get through, you might want to decide ahead of time which questions you want your group to discuss.
- In preparing for week 1 you will want to preview questions 6 and 7. Because these questions are a little more challenging, you might want to think through how you would answer both questions and then be prepared to share your answers when you get to those questions. Also, you can go to www.LivingOnTheEdge.org and find a link to some other resources that are a good complement to this series.

SESSION 2: Whatever Happened to Right & Wrong? (Part 2)

- Why not begin your preparation by praying right now for the people in your group. You might even want to keep their names in your Bible. You may also want to ask people in your group how you can pray for them specifically.
- If somebody doesn't come back this week, be sure to follow up with them. Even if you knew they were going to have to miss the group meeting, give them a call or shoot them an e-mail letting them know that they were missed. It would also be appropriate to have a couple of other people in the group let them know they were missed.
- If you haven't already previewed the video, take the time to do so. It will help you know how to best facilitate the group and what the best discussion questions are for your group.

- This week discussion question 4 will ask, "where are you or your children being subtly influenced to embrace relative truth?" Relative truth has become so prevalent in our society that many of us don't even notice it anymore. Make sure you take adequate time to talk about this issue.
- In question 6, the group will be asked how pragmatism and consumerism has infiltrated their lives, their families, and their church. Be sure that this doesn't turn into a forum for blasting a church or pastor. At the end of discussing that question your group will be asked to pray for their pastor and church leadership. Please leave time to do this.

SESSION 3: The Search for Truth About Sex (Part 1)

- Did anybody miss last week's session? If so, make it a priority to follow up and let them know they were missed. It just might be your care for them that keeps them connected to the group.
- Share the load. One of the ways to raise the sense of ownership within the group is to get them involved in more than coming to the meeting. So, get someone to help with refreshments. Find somebody else to be in charge of the prayer requests. Get someone else to be in charge of any social gathering you plan. Let someone else lead the discussion one night. Give away as much of the responsibility as possible. That is GOOD leadership.
- Think about last week's meeting for a moment. Was there anyone that didn't talk or participate? In every group there are extroverts and there are introverts. There are people who like to talk and then there are those who are quite content NOT to talk. Not everyone engages in the same way or at the same level but you do want to try and create an environment where everyone wants to participate.
- Follow up with your group this week to see how they did with the Accelerate assignment. Don't shame or embarrass anyone who didn't get to the assignment, but honestly challenge them to make this a priority in the coming week.
- Because of the nature of this week's topic, for discussion your group will be asked to split up into a men's group and a women's group. Ahead of time find someone that you can ask to lead the group you won't be leading.
- After you watch the video and get ready to break up for the discussion time, stress the importance of confidentiality within these groups. For people to share openly they must feel that the group is a "safe place." So, ask the women not to share with their husbands anything another woman said in the women's group… and ask the men not to share with their wives anything that another man shared in the men's group.

SESSION 4: The Search for Truth About Sex (Part 2)

- Don't feel any pressure to get through all the questions. As people open up and talk, don't move on too quickly. Give them the space to articulate what is going on inside them as they interact with this teaching.
- Don't be afraid of silence. When you ask people a question, give them time to think about it. Don't feel like you have to fill every quiet moment with words.
- For the discussion time this week you will once again divide up into a women's group and a men's group. Once again emphasize the importance of confidentiality.
- Question 4 this week asks "What kind of guardrails do you need to put into your life so that, as Paul said, there won't be even a hint of sexual immorality?" This is a question that could get to some very personal struggles and temptations that people deal with. Be prayed up and affirm people's courage to share where they need help.
- At the end of discussion question 7, you will be asked to have a time of prayer for one another. The goal here is not to "fix" anyone or offer advice, but rather to carry these people and their needs before the Lord.

SESSION 5: What Do You Say to a Gay Friend? (Part 1)

- Confidentiality is crucial to group life. The moment trust is breached, people will shut down. So, you may want to mention the importance of confidentiality again this week just to keep it on people's radar.
- Each time your group meets take a few minutes to update on what has happened since the last group meeting. Ask people what they are learning and putting into practice. Remember, being a disciple of Jesus means becoming a "doer of the word."
- As you begin this week's session, it would be a good idea to check in with the group regarding the Accelerate exercise that they have been challenged to do as homework. If people are doing the exercise, ask them what they have been learning and how it is impacting them. If they haven't been doing the exercise, encourage them to commit to it this next week.
- One of the consistent themes of this series is that of "truth and grace." Chip will clearly teach the truth of Scripture and what the Bible has to say about these controversial issues. But he will also do so with a heart of grace and compassion towards people. It is very important that your group discussion keep both "truth and grace" in balance.

- As you lead your group this week, be sensitive to the fact that some people in your group might be dealing with homosexuality within their family. People in your group might have a child or relative who is in a homosexual lifestyle. It might be good as you start your group meeting to acknowledge that homosexuality is not some distant issue but could be impacting families in our group and church.

SESSION 6: What Do You Say to a Gay Friend? (Part 2)

- You are now at the halfway point of this series. How is it going? How well is the group connecting? What has been going well and what needs a little work? Are there any adjustments you need to make?
- One way to deepen the level of community within your group is to spend time together outside the group meeting. If you have not already done so, plan something that will allow you to get to know each other better. Also, consider having someone else in the group take responsibility for a fellowship event.
- As you begin this week's session, do a check-in to see what people are learning and applying from this series. Don't be afraid to take some time at the beginning of your meeting to review some key ideas from the previous week's lessons.
- As you lead the discussion throughout this series, it's important to stress the absolute truth of the Bible. It's easy to let media and culture define what we believe about these issues. Emphasize that the Bible is our source of truth.
- Question 4 asks, "If someone were to come to come to you and tell you they want to get out of homosexuality, but they still struggle with thoughts and temptations, what would you say to them?" This question provides an opportunity to do some group coaching. It's not only important what we say, but how we say it. Help one another to articulate appropriate responses to the question.

SESSION 7: Understanding Abortion Today (Part 1)

- Consider sending an e-mail to each person in your group this week letting them know you prayed for them today. Also, let them know that you are grateful that they are in the group.
- Take a few minutes this week before you get into the study to talk about the impact of this series so far. Ask people what they are learning, applying and changing in their lives. For this series to have lasting impact it has to be more than just absorbing information. So, challenge your group to put what they are learning into action.

- Revisit the importance of B.I.O. this week. Reinforce the importance of people integrating these core practices in their lives. For example, talk about the priority of coming before God each day and submitting to the authority of God's truth.
- As you lead your group this week, don't assume that people in your group have been untouched by this issue. As you will learn from the teaching this week, 65% of women who have abortions identify themselves as Christians. This is not just a theological issue. For some in your group, this issue carries a lot of personal pain. So, help the group to approach this topic with great sensitivity.
- Question 2 is about a brief story Chip tells at the beginning of the session. Listen to the story carefully because you might want to retell it in your own words when you get to discussion question 2.

SESSION 8: Understanding Abortion Today (Part 2)

- Follow up questions. The only thing better than good questions are good follow up questions. Questions are like onions. Each question allows another layer to be peeled back and get beneath the surface.
- Be sure to take adequate time for prayer during your group meeting this week. Don't just tack it on at the end of the meeting simply out of obligation. Also, don't be afraid to stop the meeting and pray for someone who shares a need or a struggle.
- At the end of this week's teaching, Chip talks about God's forgiveness and healing. This is not only an important lesson for those who have had an abortion but all who have fallen into sin. A good verse to share with the group at this point would be Romans 8:1 which says there is NO condemnation for those who are in Christ Jesus.
- Question 5 asks what you would do if someone came to you and said they were considering an abortion. Remember to incorporate truth and grace in how you manage this discussion.
- The On Mission question this week asks your group to consider supporting and helping someone with an unexpected pregnancy. Ahead of the group meeting you might to contact a local crisis pregnancy center and ask them how your group could help.

SESSION 9: The Church and The Environment (Part 1)

- This might be a good week (or next week) to give someone else a chance to facilitate. Identify someone in your group who would enjoy the growth opportunity to facilitate this week. Call them in advance of the meeting to allow for preparation time.
- This week's Accelerate study comes from a great chapter in Psalm 104. Once again, challenge those in your group to do this sometime during the week. Also, challenge them to connect with someone else in the group this week to share what they learned from the Accelerate exercise.
- This week's lesson will be one of the more practical sessions that everyone can apply. One of your jobs as a leader is to help people take the "next step" in their growth and obedience. Get your group this week to commit to putting this teaching into practice.
- Question 6 this week will challenge you as a group to do something together to "explore some of God's glorious creation." Think about this ahead of the group meeting and come up with some ideas you could present to the group.

SESSION 10: The Church and The Environment (Part 2)

- Don't forget to celebrate what God has been teaching you and doing in the lives of group members. You might want to take some time at the beginning of this week's session to have people share how this series has made an impact on them.
- As this series closes, begin considering options for future series to lead for your group. Visit www.LivingOnTheEdge.org for more information about additional series taught by Chip.
- Question 5 explores Romans 8:19-21. The question asks what a couple of phrases in the passage mean. It would be a good idea for you to read a commentary or two. You could even Google search the passage and find some helpful commentary on the passage. This will help you understand more deeply what the passage is saying.
- Question 7 asks "how could you build bridges with those who are non-believers but are passionate about the environment?" Do some brainstorming with your group around this and then see if there is something you could commit to do as a group.

SESSION 11: The Church and Politics (Part 1)

- After this session, there will only be more week in the study. So be sure that you everyone is clear what your group is doing next after this study.
- As this series winds down, this is a good time to plan some kind of party or fellowship after you complete the study. Find the "party person" in your group and ask them to take on the responsibility of planning a fun experience for the group. Use this party as a time for people to share how God has used this series to grow them and change them.
- Just by looking at the title of this session, you know that it could result in some passionate discussion. You will want to set some ground rules for this session before turning on the teaching from Chip. Remind your group that this setting is not intended to discuss political parties or issues. The goal this week is to explore what the Bible says about Church and Politics.
- Your group this week will spend some time in Romans 13, the most definitive passage on Church and Government. It would be a good idea for you to read over the passage prior to your group meeting.

SESSION 12: The Church and Politics (Part 2)

- Congratulations! You have made it to the last week. Facilitating a series on controversial issues is no small task. So, thanks for your leadership and willingness to shepherd your group through this series.
- Even though this session is about Church and Politics, you might want to take some time for people to share how the entire series has made an impact on them.
- Question 4 this week comes from a quote by Chuck Colson. He said, "The danger with Christian political movements per se is that they tend to make the Gospel hostage to particular political agendas." The group will be asked the following questions in response to his statement. "What does he mean by that statement? And how can we keep from falling into this danger?" Take some time to reflect on Colson's statement and how you might answers those questions.
- One thing that is very clear from Scripture when it comes to the Church and Politics is that Christians are called upon to pray for our government leaders. Question 6 this week will encourage your group to have a time of prayer for politicians and government officials. Don't use this time to pray about issues, but rather use this time to pray them as people.

PRAYER AND PRAISE

One of the most important things you can do in your group is to pray with and for each other. Write down each other's concerns here so you can remember to pray for these requests during the week!

Use the Follow Up box to record an answer to a prayer or to write down how you might want to follow up with the person making the request. This could be a phone call, an e-mail or a card. Your personal concern will mean a lot!

DATE	PERSON	PRAYER REQUEST	FOLLOW UP

DATE	PERSON	PRAYER REQUEST	FOLLOW UP

DATE	PERSON	PRAYER REQUEST	FOLLOW UP

DATE	PERSON	PRAYER REQUEST	FOLLOW UP

DATE	PERSON	PRAYER REQUEST	FOLLOW UP

DATE	PERSON	PRAYER REQUEST	FOLLOW UP

DATE	PERSON	PRAYER REQUEST	FOLLOW UP

GROUP ROSTER

NAME	HOME PHONE	E-MAIL

WHAT'S NEXT?

Small Group Studies offered by Chip Ingram and Living on the Edge.

GOD: AS HE LONGS FOR YOU TO SEE HIM

How would you describe God? Awesome? All Powerful? Creator? While we cannot know Him exhaustively, we can know Him truly. And God longs for you to see Him as He truly is. Join Chip in this fascinating series studying the seven attributes of God.

MIRACLE OF LIFE CHANGE

Is life change really possible? If we're honest most of us would answer, "No." You've tried numerous programs that promise big changes, but in reality, deliver very little results. You long for transformation, but don't know where to begin. There's good news for you and there is hope. Life change is possible!

TRUE SPIRITUALITY

Christians today live in a world that is activity-heavy and relationship-light. The result is spiritual emptiness. We struggle to know what God wants FROM us and FOR us ... and we're unsure what a real relationship with God really looks like. The next steps of your journey toward true spirituality start here.

INVISIBLE WAR

Beneath our tangible landscape lurks an invisible spiritual realm where an unseen battle rages. It's real and it's dangerous. If you're prepared to remove the blinders and gaze into the unseen world, Chip is ready to take you there.

EFFECTIVE PARENTING IN A DEFECTIVE WORLD

Raising children is a tough challenge in today's world. Peers and pop culture exert a never-ending pressure on kids. But the good news is that God has been working with people from bad situations for a long time! In Effective Parenting you will learn how God's principles for raising children still work today. Packed with practical advice, this series will give struggling parents a vision for their children's future and life-changing help for today!

EXPERIENCING GOD'S DREAM FOR YOUR MARRIAGE

Would you like a fresh breeze to blow in your marriage? Do you long for a marriage where intimacy and communication are a reality instead of a dream? "Experiencing God's Dream for Your Marriage" is a topical series by Chip Ingram examining God's design for marriage, with practical instruction to help you make your marriage what God desires it to be.

FIVE LIES THAT RUIN RELATIONSHIPS

Have you ever looked back over a situation or relationship in your life and wondered how it became so messy or difficult? In this study, we'll define five of the most common lies that have the potential to ruin relationships with those we love. What we think about life determines how we live it, so there is power in knowing and applying God's truth.

LOVE, SEX & LASTING RELATIONSHIPS

Everyone wants to love and be loved. The pursuit of "true love" is everywhere you look! It's romanticized on TV and in the movies we watch. There are books about it, songs about it, internet dating, and even seminars on it... all of which are designed to "help" you find that special someone to love. So why is "true love" so elusive? Could it be that the picture of love we see in today's culture is nothing more than an illusion?

BALANCING LIFE'S DEMANDS

Are you busy, tired, stressed out, and stretched to the limit? Does life seem a little out of control? Are you running long on "to do's" and short on time? If so, join us in this series, Balancing Life's Demands. You'll learn how to put "first things first" and find peace in the midst of pressure and adversity. No clichés or quick fixes, just practical biblical insights to help you order your personal world.

REBUILDING YOUR BROKEN WORLD

Lives today are filled with pain. Either through stress, pressure, unfortunate circumstances or bad decisions, many of us find ourselves living in a world that has fallen apart. This series from James 1 is designed to help you begin where you are and rebuild your broken world.